Models of Language

Models of Language

I. I. REVZIN

Translated from the Russian by N. F. C. OWEN
and A. S. C. ROSS
and revised by the Author

METHUEN & CO LTD
11 NEW FETTER LANE LONDON EC4

First published as *Modeli yazyka*
by Izdatel'stvo Akademii Nauk SSSR 1962
English translation first published 1966 by Methuen & Co Ltd
11 New Fetter Lane London EC4
Printed in Great Britain by Robert Cunningham & Sons Ltd
Longbank Works, Alva

CONTENTS

FOREWORD BY A. S. C. ROSS

Linguistics consists of two parts, usually called *Descriptive* and *Comparative* respectively. Descriptive Linguistics may be defined by stating that it seeks the answers to two questions, viz. (1) What does Language resemble? and (2) How best to describe it? A rather obvious way of answering the first question is by devising one or more mathematico-logical notations which simulate Language. Until recently this has, in effect, not been done, and it was always my ambition to do it myself. Now Mr Revzin has done it in his *Modeli Yazyka* [*Models of Language*] which it therefore gives me great pleasure to translate – with the invaluable collaboration of my colleague, Mr Owen.

Mr Revzin clearly indicates the scope of his subject at the beginning of §8: "from the author's point of view, the Theory of Models of Language is that part of General Linguistics which makes use of mathematical models of Language (for whatever purposes they have been made) for: (*a*) the exposition of the range of initial concepts with which philologists operate when studying Language, and the establishment of the relations between the units determined ... (*b*) the clarification of the methods which are applied in a parallel way under different names at different levels of language research ... (*c*) the clarification of the connection between the relations in the text and the relations in the system."

TRANSLATORS' NOTES

(I) The Russian examples, etc.

Naturally, most of the author's examples are taken from Russian. We add approximate English translations as footnotes at the foot of the page[1,2,3]. We divide sentences up by means of strokes (/)[4], sometimes add words not in the Russian (such as the articles) in square brackets [ ], and occasionally give parsings in round brackets ( ). In some cases the author translates his examples into Russian and we do not give an English translation (for instance, for the French and German examples)[5]. In the case of some other languages (for instance, Indonesian and Estonian), we translate the author's Russian translation of his examples.

(II) Abbreviations[6]

acc. = accusative; adj. = adjective; Ashby = W.R.A., *An introduction to Cybernetics*; Bally = C.B., *Linguistique générale et linguistique française* (1932 ed.); *Byulleten'* = *Byulleten' obedineniya po problemam mashinnogo perevoda*; Chomsky = N.C., *Syntactic structures*; dat. = dative; def. = definite; *Doklady* = *Doklady na konferentsii po obrabotke Informatsii, mashinnomu perevodu i avtomaticheskomu chteniyu teksta*; fem. = feminine; Fitialov = S.Ya.F., "*O postroenii*

---

[1] The author's footnotes are thus relegated to pp. 161-7.

[2] We also translate his examples from some other languages (for instance, Bulgarian and Polish) of which he does not give a Russian translation.

[3] Further, parsings are sometimes given; and translations once given are not repeated in the immediate vicinity.

[4] Enclosure by two strokes indicates that the one English word corresponds to two foreign words.

[5] The author also gives a number of English examples with Russian translation.

[6] Of grammatical terms, and titles of books, articles and periodicals.

formal'noi morfologii v svyazi s mashinnym perevodom" in *Doklady* ii; gen. = genitive; Greenberg = J.G., *Essays in Linguistics*; Harris = Z.H., *Methods in Structural Linguistics*; imperf. = imperfect; indef. = indefinite; instr. = instrumental; intrans. = intransitive; Jespersen = O.J., *The Philosophy of Grammar*; Kulagina = O.S.K., "*Ob odnom sposobe opredeleniya grammaticheskikh ponyatii na baze Teorii Mnozhestv*", *PK* i, 203-14; Martinet = A.M., *Économie des changements phonétiques*; masc. = masculine; *MatP* = *Matematicheskoe prosveshchenie*; *Mélanges* = *Mélanges linguistiques publiées à l'occasion du VIIe Congrès international des Linguistes*; *MP* = *Mashinnyi perevod i prikladnaya Lingvistika*; neut. = neuter; nom. = nominative; pers. = person; Peshkovskii = A.M.P., *Russkii sintaksis v nauchnom osveshchenii* (6th ed.); *PK* = *Problemy Kibernetiki* (ed. A. A. Lyapunov); *PL* = *Primenenie Logiki v nauke i tekhnike*; pl. = plural; pres. = present; pron. = pronoun; *RevL* = *Revue de Linguistique*; sb. = noun; sg. = singular; Shcherba = L.V.Shch., *Prepodovanie inostrannykh yazykov v srednei shkole*; *STI* = *Strukturno-tipologicheskie issledovaniya*; *TCLP* = *Travaux du Cercle linguistique de Prague*; *Tezisy* = *Tezisy soveshchaniya po Matematicheskoi Lingvistike*; trans. = transitive; Trnka = B.T., "*On some problems of Neutralization*", *Omagiu lui Iorgu Iordan cu prilejul împlinirii a 70 de ani*, 861-6; Trubetzkoy = N.S.T., *Grundzüge der Phonologie* (*TCLP* vii); Tseitin = G.S.Ts., "*K voprosu o postroenii matematicheskikh modelei Yazyka*" in *Doklady* iii; Uspenskii = V.A.U., "*K opredeleniyu chasti rechi v Teoretiko-Mnozhestvennoi sisteme Yazyka*", in *Byulleten'* v; vb. = verb; *VG* = *Voprosy grammaticheskogo stroya* (ed. V. V. Vinogradov, N. A. Baskakov and N. S. Pospelov); Vinogradov = V.V.V., *Sovremennyi russkii yazyk*; *VYa* = *Voprosy Yazykoznaniya*; *Zbornik* = *Zbornik u chast Belića*.

(III) Signs

The author makes considerable use of the notation of Symbolic Logic. We give here the relevant signs, with explanations[1], and illustrative examples taken from the text[2].

(1) ∩ means "that which is common to". Thus "$K^{(1)}(x) \cap K^{(2)}(y) \neq 0$" [p.27, line 9] means "that which is common to the class $K^{(1)}(x)$

---

[1] In this connection our thanks are due to our colleague, Mr P. T. Geach.
[2] Page- and line-references in brackets ( ).

and the class $K^{(2)}(y)$ is not zero", i.e. these two classes have at least one member in common.

(2) $\cup$ means "joined with". Thus "$x = \alpha \cup m_i$" (p. 168, line 8) means "x consists of α and m_i".

(3) $\subseteq$ means "is a subclass of *or* is the whole class". Thus "$R(x) \subseteq T(x)$" (p. 81, line 16) means "the class $R(x)$ is a subclass of the class $T(x)$ *or* is the whole class $T(x)$".

(4) $\supseteq$ means "has as a subclass *or* is identical with". Thus "$B^{(1)}(x) \supseteq B^{(2)}(x)$" (p. 173, line 3) means "the class $B^{(1)}(x)$ has the class $B^{(2)}(x)$ as a subclass *or* is identical with the class $B^{(2)}(x)$".

(5) $\in$ means "is a member of". Thus "$x \in K^{(i)}(y)$" (p. 172, line 18) means "x is a member of the class $K^{(i)}(y)$".

(6) $\bar{\in}$ means "is not a member of". Thus "$x \bar{\in} K^{(j)}(y)$" (p. 172, line 18) means "x is not a member of the class $K^{(j)}(y)$".

The members of classes are frequently enumerated within braces. Thus "$K_1^{(1)} = \{p, t, k\}$" (p. 25, line 2) means "the members of the class $K_1^{(1)}$ are p, t and k"[1].

The following are some special signs used and defined in the text[2].

    (i) $\sim$ in:
        (*a*) "$\tilde{S}_1$" (§39);
        (*b*) "$x_i \, \tilde{\overline{E}} \, x_j$" (§23).
    (ii) $\rightarrow$ in "$S_i \rightarrow S_j$" (§32).
    (iii) $\Rightarrow$ in "$B \Rightarrow A$", $\rightleftarrows$ in "$A \rightleftarrows B$" (§41).

[1] So "$\Gamma(x) = \{x\}$" (p. 98, line 9) means "x is the only member of the class $\Gamma(x)$".

[2] The paragraph in which the definition occurs is given in brackets (as "(§23)").

I dedicate this book to the memory of
my father – a geologist and enthusiastic
classical philologist, who died in October 1941
at the front in the War of the Fatherland

AUTHOR'S PREFACE

The works on machine translation which began to appear in the Soviet Union from 1955 acted as a stimulus to the arising of Mathematical Linguistics, so-called, or, in other words, the application of mathematical ideas and methods in Linguistics.

The author was drawn into the discussion of the linguistic problems of machine translation by A. A. Lyapunov, and conversations with him have had a great influence on his subsequent activity. The author was fortunate in being one of the first to get to know the Theory-of-Sets system of grammatical concepts proposed by A. A. Lyapunov's pupil, O. S. Kulagina; and, later on, she helped the author in his work of developing a linguistic interpretation of this theory.

The author explained his first experiments in this direction in May 1957 in a seminar on Mathematical Linguistics in Moscow State University. Participation in this seminar, which was operating from September 1956 till May 1958 under the direction of Vyach. Vs. Ivanov, P. S. Kuznetsov and V. A. Uspenskii, helped the author gradually to overcome his original enthusiasm for the purely formal side of mathematical symbolism, and to understand that mathematical ideas in Linguistics are only fruitful where they are connected with a clear understanding of the purely linguistic side of the various phenomena. People who took part in the seminar will doubtless recognize ideas discussed in the seminar in many paragraphs.

In the academic year 1957-58 the author gave a special course in the Translation Faculty of the 1st MGPIIYa: "An introduction to Mathematical Linguistics and machine translation." Vyach. Vs. Ivanov and I. M. Yaglom became acquainted with the typescript of the course and made a number of useful observations, which have been used in the writing of this present book.

The decisive factor which determined the structure of the book and its present general trend was the author's share in the work of the Sector of Structural Typology of the Slavonic Languages of the Institute of Slavonic Studies of the Academy of Sciences of the U.S.S.R. The author's colleagues in the Sector, M. I. Burlakova, Z. M. Volotskaya, T. N. Moloshnaya, T. M. Nikolaeva, D. M. Segal, V. N. Toporov and T. V. Tsiv'yan, took the liveliest interest in discussing the book and assisted in the elimination of some of its shortcomings. Still more important was the constant contact with fellow-members of the Sector, which helped to clarify the author's point of view on a number of typological problems.

The following people also became acquainted with the final version of the manuscript: Vyach. Vs. Ivanov, O. S. Kulagina, V. Yu. Rozentsveig, G. A. Shestopal and I. Yu. Shekhter; and they made a number of extremely valuable observations.

The author regrets that he is not able to mention here all those who helped him by their contributions in the seminar on Mathematical Linguistics, in the Committee on Applied Linguistics of the Speech Section of the Commission on Acoustics of the Academy of Sciences of the U.S.S.R., in the Union on Machine Translation, at the first All-Union Conference on Machine Translation and at other meetings and conferences. The general conception of the theory of Models of Language was formed in these discussions and in private conversations. Of course, this does not mean that the author is removing from himself the responsibility for all the shortcomings of this general conception and for all the individual opinions he has put forward.

In investigating the theory of Models of Language as a linguistic theory, the author has given most attention, not to the construction of models, but to explaining the connections between the concepts of the model and the linguistic facts. Therefore, among other things, the proof of all the theorems has been put in an Appendix. And, furthermore, the author makes very scanty use of mathematical symbolism in the main part. An exception is made of some Theory-of-Sets symbols which are already fairly widely used in linguistic works.

The structure of the book can really be explained by the fact that, in it, an attempt is made to construct a linguistic, and not a mathematical theory of Models. Thus, in Chapter II, phonological models that differ little from certain grammatical ones in their structure are analysed separately. Chapter III is specially devoted to a discussion of the initial concepts of the model and their linguistic interpretation. Chapter IV is mainly devoted to a discussion of the linguistic applications of the paradigmatic models. As for the syntagmatic models (Chapter V), the author did not manage to deal with this subject as fully, but here also the connections between the models being examined and the corresponding linguistic theories are indicated as far as possible.

I Types of models of Language

§1 · *Deductive methods in Linguistics*

The question of the methods of linguistic research has recently become one of the basic problems interesting philologists. The formulation of this question arises, not only from the appearance of a series of new applications of the Science of Language (e.g. machine translation, the problem of the transmission and storage of information, etc.), but also from the internal development of Linguistics itself – and this is therefore proof that a certain degree of maturity has been attained by this science.

In every science there comes a definite time, when, after a period of very rapid development and the assimilation of a large amount of new material, after a series of magnificent discoveries, it becomes necessary, as it were, to turn back and subject to analysis the very basis of the science, i.e. those fundamental concepts with which it operates. Most characteristic in this respect has been the development of Mathematics – a science to which Linguistics has recently drawn closer both in practice and theory. This is how Professor A. Ya. Khinchin describes the situation in Mathematics towards the beginning of the nineteenth century:

"This was a peculiar picture: not one of the most fundamental concepts of Analysis had been defined with any exactitude; the question of what an infinitely small quantity was was subjected to innumerable discussions – from the point of view of its logical basis quite fruitlessly, for, in the majority of cases, not one of the disputing parties could offer anything except hazy images, not binding upon it."[1]1

Finally, scholars realized that Mathematics could not develop as a science without a firm logical foundation. The enormous achievements of modern Mathematics, right up to the creation of electronic

[1] [Translation – *N.F.C.O. and A.S.C.R.*]

calculating machines, would have been unthinkable without that revision of the logical foundations of the science which was carried through in the nineteenth century.

Linguistics is suffering an analogous fate. Carried away by the great achievements of Historical Linguistics which were bound up with the application of the comparative-historical method, scholars of the nineteenth century hardly considered the exact meaning of terms such as "speech-sound", "morpheme", "word" or "sentence". F. de Saussure was quite right when he said "en matière de langue on s'est toujours contenté d'opérer sur des unités mal définies".[2] It was only a complete revolution in Linguistics, caused in the first place by F. de Saussure's own works, which made philologists really start thinking about the basic concepts with which they operated.

As is well known, every science uses abstractions, however different the routes leading to the formation of these abstractions may be. Some sciences, e.g. Geology, Botany, Chemistry, Physics, start from actual facts, observed in Nature, and, by generalizing these observed facts, pass from the particular to the general; other sciences, such as Mathematics and Logic, go out from general abstract truths, taken a priori, to the establishment of particular facts. Of course, there are no purely inductive or purely deductive sciences. Thus, Chemistry and Physics, in their modern form, contain a very essential deductive part; on the other hand, even in Mathematics, an element of induction plays a basic part.[3] All the same, it is useful to distinguish deductive and inductive sciences according to which methods are prevalent in a given science. In that case, where should we place Linguistics? By its very nature, Linguistics should make use of inductive methods first of all; it describes the actual facts of speech in actual languages; in fact, it is the "field work" of the philologist which has the greatest value.

On the other hand, the existence of an infinite number of acts of speaking for the philologist to study hardly allows him the possibility of formulating the basic concepts of the Science of Language by generalization from induction.

Hence it follows that philologists need not only inductive, but also deductive methods of research in order to obtain a system of general concepts to help them to make sense of the data obtained by the analysis of actual languages. Besides, the new technical applications of Language make necessary the construction of very strict deductive systems which will satisfy modern scientific demands.

In its deductive part, Linguistics, it seems, can be constructed just as Logic or Mathematics are constructed; a certain minimal quantity of primary indefinable terms is established, and all the rest of the terms are defined by means of the primary ones. At the same time certain primary statements as to the connections between these terms (axioms) should be clearly formulated and all other statements should be proved, i.e. reduced to certain other statements.

Many of the disputes about Mathematical Linguistics which have taken place during recent years have been concerned with the question whether this Science of Language can be constructed in such a way. Without anticipating a final solution of this dispute, which belongs to the future, it is possible to say that, at present, it is not clear how all the great variety of the rather contradictory facts of speech-reality, as they are described in the many grammars of actual languages, may be placed in the framework of a strict deductive theory.

Such a conclusion does not, however, give occasion for pessimism. Modern Science possesses a powerful instrument for discovering the complicated phenomena of actual reality – the method of making models, the essence of which is the construction of a certain sequence of abstract schemes which should be a more or less close approximation to the data of actual reality.[4]

The method of making models is useful mainly when it is applied in the first place to that part of Linguistics which has, since de Saussure's day, come to be known as the "internal" part. Further, it is necessary at the start to examine general models not connected with the peculiarities of actual languages, and this will help, later on, in the modelling of separate groups of languages and also, perhaps, of actual languages themselves. Thus, the modelling of a language as it is understood in this book is a method in which the investigator proceeds from certain of the most general features of actual languages, formulates certain hypotheses dealing with the structure of the language as an abstract semiotic system, and then establishes what is the relationship between the consequences of these hypotheses and the facts of actual languages as described by actual linguistic disciplines.

§2 · *The model and its interpretation · The general form of the model of Language*

The model is constructed in the following manner. Out of all the great variety of concepts accumulated by the science, certain ones which can conveniently be regarded as primary are selected. Certain relations between these primary concepts are determined and these may be adopted in the character of postulates. All the remaining statements are drawn up on a strictly deductive basis in terms defined, ultimately, by means of the primary concepts.

It is clear that the term "model" in this sense does not in any way correspond to Sapir's "pattern". A model in this sense is not a part of Language as a system, but itself represents a certain hypothetical scientific construction, a certain construct.[5]

It is essential strictly to distinguish the model (that is, a certain abstract object, not dependent on the nature of its elements) and its linguistic interpretation. (In order to distinguish the concepts relating to the model and those relating to its linguistic interpretation, we shall from now on (as far as possible) use two sets of different terms: for the concepts of the model, terms used in Mathematics, and for its interpretation, terms used in Linguistics.) Several different linguistic interpretations of one and the same model are possible (for instance, a phonological one and a grammatical one).

The interrelations between a model and its interpretations are complex and varied. The model, as has already been pointed out, is an abstract construction, whereas "the problem of interpretation is that of substituting something precise".[6] For Linguistics this means the substitution of real linguistic objects for terms of the model. We may note that the following remark of B. Russell's is very much to the point for the theory of linguistic models:

"The question of interpretation has been unduly neglected. So long as we remain in the region of mathematical formulae, everything appears precise, but when we seek to interpret them it turns out that the precision is partly illusory. Until this matter has been cleared up, we cannot tell with any exactitude what any given science is asserting."[7]

Until the interpretation of a particular linguistic model has been investigated, the model itself remains a pure fiction. Indeed, proof obtained by the deductive route, however irreproachable from the logical point of view it may be, still tells us nothing about the nature of the actual language described by the model. Only if definite correspondences between the original and the model[8] obtain, can we speak of the convincingness of the model. Practicalness is the only possible criterion for this correspondence; it is for this reason that machine translation and other practical applications of Linguistics acquire such importance for the theory of models.

On the other hand, the investigation of the linguistic interpretations of a model is extremely important for the clarification of the conditions for more exact and complete correspondence between the model and the original, i.e. the intensification of the notional value of models.

Later we shall see what rôle in the development of the Theory of Models is played by a statement of the inadequacy of any particular model in relation to the facts of actual languages.

Now we pass on to an outline of the initial primary concepts from which the majority of linguistic models is constructed.

First of all we note that, as distinct for example from Acoustic Phonetics, which deals with a definite continuum,[9] the theory of Models of Language always deals with certain discrete units. On this basis Joos in general regards Linguistics as a branch of "discrete Mathematics".[10] As we shall see below, the Theory of Models can be regarded as a purely linguistic theory; nevertheless the recognition of the discrete character of any linguistic model is extremely important.[11]

In all Models of Language the concept of a certain element is taken as the point of departure. Depending on the level of Language which is being subjected to the modelling, this initial element will be interpreted as a separate sound (at the phonetic level) or as a word-form (at the syntactic level).

The second important concept is that of the Sequence. We call any ordered succession of elements a *sequence* – $A = x_1\ x_2 \ldots x_i \ldots x_n$. We divide all sequences into two classes: we shall call sequences of the first class *registered* (in the interpretation, that is sequences belonging to a given language), and sequences of the second class *unregistered* (that is sequences not belonging to the given language). Like the concept of the "element", the concept "sequence" receives a different interpretation depending on the level of investigation of the language. At the phonological level, by the "registered sequence" we understand the "phonetic word". At the syntactic level we interpret the sequence as the phrase. In so far, however, as the concept of the registered phrase allows varied interpretation, we simply assume that the phrases being considered in a certain model have already been given us from without.

We emphasize this circumstance by using the term "registered phrase".

It is natural to divide all models of Language into four basic types depending on whether the number of elements is finite and the length of the registered sequence limited.[12]

1) the number of elements is finite and the length of the registered sequence is limited;

2) the number of elements is finite and the length of the registered sequence is not limited;

3) the number of elements is infinite and the length of the registered sequence is limited;

4) the number of elements is infinite and the length of the registered sequence is not limited.

Each of the types of models enumerated sets the investigator its own logical problems. We shall only consider models in which the number of elements is finite. As regards the length of the sequence: we shall not at first impose any restriction on it, and, thereafter, we shall see what difference there is between the model of the first class and the model of the second class.

The concept of the division of a set of elements into subsets is an essential initial (sometimes derivative) concept of the Model of Language. To put it another way, a certain system of subsets of the initial set is usually taken as given, and for each element it is indicated to which sets it belongs. These subsets may, generally speaking, overlap – of this kind are the marks in Phonology or the Categories in Grammar.

The majority of models are constructed so that they are based on this initial division – but so as to obtain a division consisting of classes which do not overlap. Sometimes a division into classes which do not overlap is given as a supplement. One way or another all the models under consideration can be reduced to the concepts that have been outlined here – element, sequence and certain divisions of the set of initial elements.

§3 · *Analytic and synthetic models*

The logical structure of every model is such that, in it, we are dealing with certain formal operations on certain sets of objects. With regard to the operations permissible in a given model, all objects are divided into three kinds: (*a*) initial objects, to which certain operations may be applied, but which do not themselves arise as a result of any operations (being given from without); (*b*) intermediate objects, to which operations are applied and which themselves arise because of the application of operations; (*c*) final objects, which arise as a result of operations, but to which operations are not applied.

We shall say that model A is the *reciprocal* model with respect to model B, if the objects which are initial in A are final objects in B, and, conversely, the initial objects of B are the final objects of A. We shall provisionally call the construction of the model which is reciprocal with respect to A the *inversion* of A.

We shall divide models of Language into *analytic* (or "analysing"[13]) models and those which are reciprocal with respect to them, namely *synthetic* (or "synthesizing") models, depending on whether we start from a set of registered sequences (the analytic model) or obtain the registered sequences as a result of certain operations (the synthetic model, or, as it is sometimes called, the model of generation). Each time, we shall start with a consideration of the analytic models and immediately indicate the corresponding synthetic one. To a certain extent the analytic models formalize the situation which is examined in Descriptive Linguistics (for instance, Harris's[14] "universe of discourse" corresponds to the concept of the set of registered sequences). Grammars of generation[15] have recently begun to be constructed on the basis of the concepts of Descriptive Linguistics.

These two forms of models, analytic and synthetic, correspond to two possible forms of linguistic description; the one route is from the facts of speech to the system of the language and the second is from the system of the language to the facts of speech. To a certain extent they also correspond to the two aspects of the act of communication: hearing ("analysis") and speaking ("synthesis"); and it has more than once been noted that different types of description must correspond to these aspects (cf. the distinction between Jespersen's[16] "morphology" and "syntax", between

Shcherba's[17] "passive" and "active" grammar, between Mathesius's[18] "linguistic decipherment" and "linguistic stylization", and Jakobson's[19] indication of the different character of the phonological units corresponding to the two aspects). Hockett's[20] distinction between the two approaches to linguistic analysis is also close to the division into analytic and synthetic models: models in which we start from certain units and their interrelations in a text ("item and arrangement") and models in which we begin with certain units and a certain process which makes it possible for us to obtain new units ("item and process").

The following is one of the cardinal facts of the theory of linguistic models: one and the same set of registered sequences may be generated by two different synthetic models (the simplest example of such non-uniqueness was constructed by Greenberg[21]). This fact means that one and the same language (as a certain set of registered sequences) may be described by several different grammars. Greenberg suggested calling an assembly of registered sequences which can be described with the help of the various rules of generation a "heteronomic sign-system". "Heteronomy" in this sense is also a generalization of the phenomenon of the homonym in the case when the units consist of a whole sign-system. In Greenberg's example heteronomy arises because of the indeterminateness of the initial units and the permissible operations. However, logically, heteronomy is not excluded in the more definitely given model either.

So it is useful to indicate which synthetic model corresponds to any particular analytic one. In general, the phenomenon of heteronomy (and some other facts with which we shall become acquainted later) show that synthetic models are more convenient for the description of Language than analytic models. On the other hand, we shall see that the construction of reasonable synthetic models always presupposes the presence of well-elaborated analytic models. The combined examination of analytic and synthetic models is also important from the point of view of the interpretation of a model and the evaluation of its degree of adequacy.

The acceptability of an analytic model may be evaluated according to the extent to which the concepts formulated within it reflect the systemic relations within the language. But it is evident that it is precisely the description of the systemic relations in the language which is attended with considerable difficulties and is far from simple.

It is easier to evaluate the acceptability of a synthetic model; we examine the set of sequences generated by the given model, and compare it with the set of phrases actually existing in the given language. If one model produces more registered phrases and fewer unregistered phrases[22] than another, then it is obviously better. If two models generate the same set of phrases, then they may be regarded as equivalent – and so on. Starting from this consideration, N. Chomsky, in the work we have mentioned, constructed a series of models such that each successive model produces all the phrases of the preceding one, but the converse does not take place.

This question is posed, in a general form, by S. Tseitin in the work mentioned; he writes: "It is possible to make the problem of approximating to a language by models more precise by introducing the concept of the convergence of the succession of models to the language, which, we say, could be defined in the modelling of the set of grammatically correct phrases in the following way: we say that the succession of models converges to the language if every grammatically correct phrase is also correct in all the models of the succession, beginning from a certain place; and every succession of signs which is not a grammatically correct phrase is not this in all the models of the succession, starting from the particular place."[23][1]

In conclusion, we observe that the choice of a model also depends on the character of the material being investigated. If the set of registered phrases is infinite, the analytic model plays only an auxiliary theoretical rôle, helping with the clarification of the concepts, but it cannot be applied directly. If however the set of registered phrases is finite, the analytic model is apparently more suitable for practical application than the synthetic one. We return to this question in §43; here, however, we note that the difference in the linguistic approach to a finite or infinite set of phrases in connection with analysis or synthesis was already noticed by L. V. Shcherba, who wrote: "In the dead languages . . . in practice there are no processes of speaking and understanding given; on the other hand we have materially objectivized language material in the form of texts . . . Here the distinction between dead and living languages explains among other things the relative ease of investigating the first, where there is a finite amount of objectivized language material, and the great difficulty of investigating the second, where the material is infinite and difficult to objectivize."[24][1]

[1] [Translation – *N.F.C.O. and A.S.C.R.*]

§4 · *Discriminating models*

There is a special type of model in which both a set of registered sequences and a system of generation are regarded as given, and the process of transition from sequence to system is examined, i.e. the means by which this transition is made in a minimum number of steps is examined.

The most detailed model of such a type – applied to the Russian language – has been described by T. M. Nikolaeva.[25]

It is clear that models of this type have very great practical importance (machine translation, foreign language teaching, etc.).

The construction of discriminating models has also considerable theoretical significance; in fact, the essence of such a model is that the units of the synthesis are reconstructed by analysis. This corresponds to the latest cybernetic representations as to the nature of speech comprehension, which have recently been developed by L. A. Chistovich.[26] According to these representations, in speech-analysis, it is necessary to reconstruct the instructions which led to the generation of a given speech-segment.

§5 · *Paradigmatic and syntagmatic models*

Models of Language can also be classified from another point of view, namely from the point of view of the relations in Language which they reflect. Some of them can provisionally be called *paradigmatic* and others *syntagmatic*. To the paradigmatic models there belong those in which we investigate the principles which unite certain elements into classes (separate sounds into phonemes, separate morphs into morphemes, separate words into categories and parts of speech) and which establish the relations in a system. Syntagmatic models are those in which the relations between elements (phonemes, words) in a certain stipulated sequence, that is, in speech, are investigated. As is well-known, both aspects in Language (the syntagmatic and the paradigmatic) are bound together in the closest fashion. Thus, on the one hand, efforts are made to deduce paradigmatic relations from syntagmatic ones. On the other hand, it is more useful to build syntagmatic models after the elements have been united into classes, as this simplifies the description.

The importance of paradigmatic models is that they allow us to model the systemic relations in Language. On the basis of para-digmatic models we can obtain dynamic models, which examine Language as a system in transition from one steady state to another. It is clear that it is just such models that are needed for the inculcation of cybernetic ideas into the comparative-historical study of languages.

§6 · *Models of Language and the Statistics of Speech*

The method of making models, as a method of the deductive analysis of Language, can also render help by introducing into Linguistics exact inductive methods, that is Statistics.

In its turn, the making of models of Language must be linked with a consideration of its statistical structure. This follows from the ensuing considerations.

First of all, a model has in view a certain ideal object; the correspondence of this ideal object with the relations of reality actually existing is always more or less relative, and the degree of this correspondence must be clarified statistically. We shall see further on that, wherever there arises a transition from the definitions of an abstract model to the application of these definitions to the analysis of actual Language, statistical criteria play a part, explicit or implicit. And, indeed, it could not be otherwise. In Language, categories of any sort are essentially determined on the basis of statistical criteria. If a model is to describe accurately the true reality of actual Language, then the groupings determined in it must correspond to those which are statistically determined in Language.

Secondly, any model makes use explicitly or implicitly of the concept of the initial speech-material (a certain set of words or phrases). This initial speech-material always consists of a certain part of the language. Even if a model has in view an infinite set of sequences, in the transition from the model to the analysis of the actual material, we once again encounter a certain finite set, or to speak statistically, a certain "sample". The question of what should be the size of this sample is a typically statistical question.

Thirdly, in models, there figure such logical terms as "all", for instance, "all phrases of the form . . .". As soon as we proceed to the application of the model, the statistical term "a sufficiently large number" becomes the correlate of this term (cf. §43).

Fourthly, when we have a certain series of models describing one and the same object, the question of assessing their efficiency arises. This question has a very important statistical aspect as well as its purely logical side (cf. §3).

Fifthly, the basic concept of the model, i.e. "the registration of a phrase", must also be interpreted on the basis of statistical considerations. As a result of the peculiar "presumption of meaningfulness" there is always the probability that a phrase which we consider "unregistered" will be interpreted by some number of persons as being meaningful, and only after a considerable number of experiments is it possible to attribute to every phrase the probability of its being meaningful.[27]

It is true that, in the present work, questions of Linguistic Statistics will not be specially singled out, but it ought always to be remembered that there is an essential connection between making models and Statistics.

§7 · *The Theory of Models and the structural typology of languages*

The importance of the new, exact methods for the typology of languages is emphasized in works devoted to the contemporary state of typological investigations.[28] The method of making models[29] has, it seems, a special place here. We have already said that any model is different from an actual language and that it is possible to describe a language exactly only by means of a succession of models, perhaps even an infinite one. It is however exceptionally important that different languages be distinguished from a given model in different ways. Thus a model becomes an objective standard for the comparison of individual languages one with another.

This method may, it seems, show itself to be particularly useful for the study of closely related languages, e.g. the Slavonic languages, for, here, many criteria which have been investigated up to now and which are connected, for instance, with the structure of the word lead to trivial results. Further on, we shall satisfy ourselves, by a series of examples, that making models helps in the typological comparison of languages.

It appears that, ultimately, the Theory of Models is connected with the typology of languages in another way also, i.e. from the point of view of constructing a general typology of sign-systems. A remarkable idea is put forward by A. A. Zaliznyak, Vyach. Vs. Ivanov and V. N. Toporov, namely that it is possible to consider every language as a modelling system in connection with which a whole hierarchy of models can be constructed beginning with abstract ones having comparatively little modelling ability but which embrace a wide range of material (models of precisely this type are considered in the chapters following) and finishing with models with a high degree of modelling ability but with a very limited objective range.

With such a formulation of the problem interesting us in this work, the question of the relationship between the model and its linguistic interpretation is one of transition from one level of making models to another.

§8 · *The Theory of Models as a linguistic theory*

The theory of models of Language represents, it seems, a purely logical interest, perhaps, even a mathematical one. Thus, with reference to the models which are considered in Chapter V of the present book, Y. Bar-Hillel says: "there exist highly interesting connections between the theory of linguistic models and such theories as the theory of automata, recursive function theory (perhaps especially conspicuous in the form of the theory of algorithms) and the theory of Post canonical systems. This multiple relationship indicates that we have, in all probability, in the theory of language models an interesting new field in which cross-fertilization of mathematical logic and structural linguistics should lead to important results."[30]

However, in our work, the theory of linguistic models is considered neither as a mathematical theory nor as a logical one, but as a *linguistic theory*.

And, indeed, from the author's point of view, the Theory of Models of Language is that part of General Linguistics which makes use of mathematical models of Language (for whatever purposes they have been made) for:

a) the exposition of the range of initial concepts with which philologists operate when studying Language, and the establishment of the relations between the units determined (cf. the range of

ML C

problems connected with the construction of a so-called Axiomatics of Linguistics);

b) the clarification of the methods which are applied in a parallel way under different names at different levels of language research (cf. the range of problems connected with the concept of "iso-morphism" in Linguistics);

c) the clarification of the connection between the relations in the text and the relations in the system (cf. the range of problems raised in the so-called Glossematics).

On the other hand, the Theory of Models of Language must help establish which of the methods of describing Language offered by philologists can already be formalized today, and which require the creation of new models capable of reflecting the more complicated constructions used in Linguistics.

II Methods of making models in Phonology

*§9 · The basic concepts in the construction of
phonological models and their linguistic interpretation*

In the investigation of the phonetic phenomena of speech and their
ultimate phonological interpretation, we are dealing with the following initial objects:

1) We are given certain initial elements, i.e. the speech-sounds.[1]

2) We are given a certain assembly of *phonetic categories* or
marks, i.e. voicedness, voicelessness, softness, hardness, fricativeness,
stopping, openness, closeness, etc.[2]

Every speech-sound is coordinated with a subset of the set of
marks. To use more ordinary terminology, we shall say that every
sound consists of *n* marks.

3) We are given certain registered sequences of speech-sounds,
which are interpreted as *phonetic words*.

It must at once be pointed out that such an interpretation is bound
up with semantic difficulty. The fact is that two conceptions of the
phonetic word, different in principle, are possible.

Interpretation 1. By a phonetic word is meant a *minimal segment
between two pauses in an actually existing speech-segment of a given
language*. This Interpretation is usually kept in view in Phonology
as well, where, for instance, the basic criterion for determining units
consists in the comparison of two actual phonetic words (or even
lexical words).

Interpretation 2. *A minimal combination of speech-sounds permissible in a given language between two pauses* is called a phonetic
word. The concept of permissibility is clearly insufficiently formal.
It is not clear to what extent it is possible to include here cases of
'meaningless language", for instance:

> Dyr byl shyl
> Ubeshur
> (Kruchenykh)

Generally speaking, it should be remembered that, for the composition of verses in meaningless language, the poet does not take just any permissible combinations, but, as a rule, those which are avoided in natural speech,[3] cf.:

> Bobeobi pelis' guby
> Veoemi pelis' vzory[1]
> (Khlebnikov)

We shall call a combination of sounds *permissible* in a given language if every element of this combination is encountered in some actually stipulated word of the given language in the same environment as in the given combination. By this definition the fragment from Kruchenykh consists of phonetic words, but *veoemi* is not a phonetic word of Russian.

Such a definition will ultimately allow us to pass easily from Interpretation 1 to Interpretation 2 (the words "at least one phonetic word according to Interpretation 1" correspond to "any phonetic word according to Interpretation 2").

Interpretation 2 is more convenient than the first one for making models, for the following reasons:

1) the concept of lexical and grammatical meaning is unsuitable for being taken into consideration, since the initial situation becomes complicated; but the basic difference between the phonetic word in the two models is that, in Interpretation 2, words do not necessarily have lexical and grammatical meaning;

2) the phonologist must take into consideration, not only the combinations realized in the words of a language, but also potential combinations of speech-sounds. As is well-known, such combinations vary a great deal from language to language and therefore have an independent interest. Furthermore, the enrichment of vocabulary by way of non-literary borrowing takes place, as a rule, in such a way that selection is made of potentially possible combinations of the speech-sounds of the one language which are more or less similar to the word of the other.[4]

3) in constructing a generating model (as we see in §16) the

[1] [The] lips sang *bobeobi*, [the] glances sang *veoemi*.

generation of phonetic words only, under Interpretation 1, is impossible.

4) in making models it is useful to describe the phenomena of Phonology and Grammar in a more or less parallel way. Nevertheless the description of the set of registered sequences in §21 corresponds to Interpretation 2.

Starting from what has been said, we shall take into consideration Interpretation 2 of the initial material. If however we sometimes use Interpretation 1 to make things easier to understand, there will be constructed only definitions for which Interpretation 1 can be easily reduced to Interpretation 2 by virtue of the comment made above.

It is essential to take account of the fact that the choice of Interpretation 2 as basic limits our possibilities. We shall no longer ultimately be able to define "the phoneme" as the smallest unit serving for the differentiation of meaning. It is possible to show, however, that such a definition leads to an unnecessary formal difficulty.[5] On the other hand, starting from the phenomenon of distribution, it is possible to define a unit in the initial material given us sufficiently close to what is usually regarded as a phoneme. This conception of the phoneme – extremely fruitful from the point of view of the ultimate formalization – was first put forward by Jones, who wrote: "If two sounds of a language can occur in the same position in respect to surrounding sounds, then *by definition* the two sounds belong to separate phonemes."[6]

It is just this concept of the phoneme which lies ultimately at the basis of the construction of the phonological models in the present work too. Since Phonology is the most developed abstract domain of the study of language, the reader must not expect here anything essentially new vis-à-vis the works of the classical writers on Phonology. The present chapter should prepare us, by means of better-known material, for the understanding of the material of the following chapters. Nevertheless, the author hopes that the series of formulations will be accepted as a useful exactifying of phonological concepts.

10 · The two classifications of phonemic marks · The phoneme and the archiphoneme

Phonetic marks can be classified with respect to *isolated sounds* and *sounds in the flow of speech*. We turn first of all to separate sounds. Suppose a language, given by the three initial concepts of §9, be analysed.

We shall describe two marks as *consistent* in a given language, if there exists at least one speech-sound in which they appear together (in other words, if both fall into a subset of marks coordinated with a certain speech-sound; later the reader can himself, in case of necessity, translate all the formulations of this paragraph into the language of correspondences).

In the opposite case we shall speak of the inconsistency of the marks. Examples of consistent marks in Russian are: voicelessness and fricativeness, voicedness and softness, etc. Examples of inconsistent marks are: voicelessness and voicing, softness and hardness, hardness and openness. Inconsistent marks may be *homogeneous* and *non-homogeneous*.

We call two inconsistent marks m_i and m_j homogeneous if there exists at least one sound of the given language such that the replacement of m_j by m_i (or m_i by m_j) also produces a sound of the given language.

Examples of homogeneous marks in Russian are: voicelessness and voicedness; high, mid- and low tongue raising; softness and hardness. Hardness and openness, for instance, are non-homogeneous inconsistent marks.

Note. In the above-mentioned system of acoustic marks of R. Jakobson (see footnote 2 on p. 162), it seems that any two inconsistent marks are homogeneous.

We turn now to the classification of marks in the flow of speech. We have agreed that every sound can be represented in the form of an assembly of marks. Under these circumstances, every phonetic word is an ordered succession of assemblies of marks. For generality, we shall consider that the pause, too, is a speech-sound, coordinated with the mark "silence" (or, consisting of the one mark "silence").

Let us consider a permissible combination of sounds in a given language (it would be most convenient to interpret "permissible combination" as "syllable", but, unfortunately, this concept is difficult to subject to modelling[7]).

If, in the given permissible pair of sounds $S_1 S_2$, one of the marks (let this be the mark *m*) of the sound S_1 (or S_2) may not be replaced by any other such that, once again, a permissible combination of sounds is obtained, then we shall say that the given mark *m* is *bound* in the given pair. Consider now the sound S_1 and examine: (1) the set of all pairs in which this sound stands in the first position, and (2) the set of all pairs in which this sound stands in the second position. If the mark *m* is bound in one or both of these sets, we shall call this mark *non-relevant*. We shall call the remaining marks *relevant* (it is obvious that the "relevant mark" so defined is a much wider concept than the "differential mark").

As an example we consider the sounds ɛ and *e* in Russian. As is well-known, they differ by one mark, openness or the corresponding closeness. Consider now all the pairs with *e* in the first position, e.g. *et'* (in эти)[1], *ed'* (in веди)[2], *en'* (in тень)[3], etc. In all these pairs the mark of closeness is bound (it is impossible to replace the mark "closeness" by that of "openness" without changing the second sound of the pair as well).

If we take all the pairs in which ɛ occurs, its replacement by *e* again leads to a non-permissible combination. Therefore we regard both marks as non-relevant.

In order that it may be plain that our principle is not different from that accepted in phonological literature, we repeat below, in almost the very same words, the argument put forward by R. I. Avanesov.[8] Consider the words *s'àt'*[4] and *s'n'àt'*[5]. The sound *s'* is characterized by the marks: dental, fricative, voiceless, soft. The first three marks are not bound in the pairs *s'â* and *s'n'* (cf. *p'at'*[6], *p'n'à*[7], *gàt'*[8], *agn'à*[9], *z'àt'*[10], *maz'n'à*[11]). As regards the mark "softness" in the sound *s'*, it is not bound in the pair *s'à* (cf. *pisàt'*[12]), but in the pair *s'n'* this mark is bound as the pair *sn'* is non-permissible. Thus the mark of softness is *s'* is not bound in some pairs and is bound in others; therefore it is regarded as relevant.

If a relevant mark is bound in a given combination, we shall call the given combination the *position of neutralization of contrast* of the given mark and of all those homogeneous with it.

For example, the position before the pause in Russian is the posi-

[1] these   [2] lead!   [3] shade   [4] sit down!
[5] to take away   [6] five   [7] stump (*gen. sg.*)
[8] kind of road   [9] fire (*gen. sg.*)   [10] son-in-law
[11] tarred with the same brush (*nom. sg. fem.*)   [12] to write

tion of neutralization of contrast of the marks voicedness and voicelessness.

Finally, we shall call a *phoneme* any assembly of relevant non-homogeneous marks coordinated with a certain speech-sound. Two sounds corresponding to one phoneme are called *allophones* or *variants* of the one phoneme.

It appears that what is understood by a *phoneme* in the school of L. V. Shcherba – and particularly by his pupils[9] – coincides in practice with that postulated by our model.

Later on we shall need yet another concept, the concept of the "archiphoneme". The archiphoneme is usually understood as being the assembly of relevant marks common to two phonemes.[10]

Let there be two different phonemes each of which comprises n marks. Let $n-1$ marks in them coincide. Then we shall call this assembly of $n-1$ marks an *archiphoneme*.

Usually there are considered only archiphonemes for which at least one of the marks differentiating the two phonemes has a position of neutralization. For instance, in Russian, the archiphoneme "non-nasal, dental, stopped, hard" is considered as the assembly of marks common to the pair of phonemes d and t, since the homogeneous marks voicedness and voicelessness have a position of neutralization.

In our model we shall use the term "real archiphoneme" for the case just considered. However, in general, we shall simply speak of archiphonemes without specifying whether they are real or not. If two phonemes have a common real archiphoneme, i.e. differ only in that the mark m_i is present in one and the mark m_j in the other, we shall say that they belong to one *elementary phonological category*.

§11 · *The phoneme in the Moscow Phonological School and its formal analogue*

There exists another important unit of the phonological system, which is considered by the Moscow Phonological School, and which is also called a "phoneme" in it, or, as R. I. Avanesov better expresses it, a "phonemic series".[11] We shall make use of this last term later on. However, it is essential to remember that, strictly speaking, we only want to construct a formal (distributive) analogue for the "phonemic series".

First of all, we shall introduce one auxiliary concept. We shall say that the phoneme F_1 *dominates* the phoneme F_2, if there exists at least one phonetic word in which F_1 can be replaced by F_2, and at least one phonetic word in which F_2 cannot be replaced by F_1.

Thus, in Russian, *o* can be replaced by *a* in the word *gody*[1], giving *gady*[2], but *a* cannot be replaced by *o* in *vada*[3]. Therefore *o* dominates *a*. Another example: *g* can be replaced by *k* in the word *gara*[4], giving *kara*[5], but *k* cannot be replaced by *g* in the word *pirok*[6]. Therefore *g* dominates *k*. It is evident that *d* also dominates *k* (cf. *dom*[7] and *kom*[8], but only *pirok*). In connection with this we shall introduce a new definition.

We shall say that the phoneme F_1 *absolutely dominates* F_2, if any other phoneme F_i dominating F_2 is distinguished from F_2 by a greater number of marks than F_1. If F_1 absolutely dominates F_2, we shall say that F_1 and F_2 belong to one phonemic series.

For instance, *g* belongs to the same phonemic series as *k*. Here, the phonemic series coincides with the elementary category, and, at first glance, we have not obtained anything new.

But the same principle can, it appears, also be applied to the analysis of Russian vowels, for which the theory of the Moscow Phonological School indeed acquires real value.

In fact, *o* absolutely dominates *a*, and both phonemes belong to one phonemic series, although, according to our exposition of the system of marks, they do not belong to one elementary category, as they differ by more than one mark.

It is necessary to have in mind once again the fact that we have not given a definition for the phonemic series in R. I. Avanesov's sense, but that we have constructed a formal analogue of this concept. The object has only been to show that the analysis of purely distributive features corresponding to a real unit is quite possible.

§12 · *A paradigmatic model*

We now enter upon the analysis of the relations between phonemes, and we shall now be interested, not in the relations in Speech, but in the relations in the system, i.e. in the paradigmatic relations. A detailed investigation of the paradigms of phonemes was carried out by N. S. Trubetzkoy in his *Grundzüge der Phonologie*. We shall limit ourselves to a very simple situation, one more convenient from the point of view of making models.

Consider all the phonemes of a given language having exactly *k* marks each. These phonemes constitute a phonological subsystem. Later we shall deal with this stipulated subsystem.

Note. In R. Jakobson's system of acoustic marks, it appears that all the phonemes belong to one subsystem.

The desire somehow to arrange the phonemes into subsystems is

[1] years   [2] reptiles   [3] water
[4] mountain   [5] punishment   [6] pie   [7] house   [8] lump

a natural one. In phonological literature it is usual to give tables in which each phoneme corresponds to the intersection of a series of marks (in the system suggested by R. Jakobson the table is replaced by the so-called matrix of identification).

For example, the subsystem of the obstruents of Russian may be represented by a table with the following (somewhat simplified) marks:

		Labial		Front-Tongue		Mid-Tongue		Back-Tongue	
		voiceless	voiced	voiceless	voiced	voiceless	voiced	voiceless	voiced
Stop	hard	p	b	t	d			k	g
	soft	p'	b'	t'	d'			k'	g'
Spirant	hard	f	v	s	z	$š$	$ž$	ch	
	soft	f'	v'	s'	z'	$š$'	$ž$'		
Affricate	hard			c		$č$			
	soft								

Such tables are very convenient for practical use (in particular, the reader is recommended later on to compare the constructions suggested below with this table). However, such tables have the drawback of it being difficult to get an idea from them of the groupings of the phonemes into particular classes and of the relations between these classes. Therefore, later on, a somewhat more complicated, but from the above point of view more convenient way of arranging the phonemes is suggested. It is given by an instruction (an "algorithm") consisting of six points.

1) We choose two phonemes having a common archiphoneme α_1 and we add to this class all the other phonemes having the given archiphoneme. We obtain the phonological class $K(\alpha_1)=K_1$. We notice that any such class is defined uniquely by an arbitrary phoneme x which belongs to it; for this reason we shall sometimes denote the class to which the phoneme x belongs as $K(x)$.

Example. From our subsystem consider the phonemes p and t. The archiphoneme consisting of the marks "stop", "voiceless", "hard" belongs to both phonemes. They are distinguished by the marks "labial" for p and "front-tongue" for t. We add to these the phoneme k as well, as it has the same archiphoneme. With these three phonemes the class of phonemes having the given archiphoneme is exhausted. As we agreed above this class may be denoted by $K(p)$ or $K(t)$ or $K(k)$.

2) Let i classes already have been constructed. We take from the remaining phonemes the maximum assembly of phonemes such that: (*a*) all of them have the common archiphoneme α_{i+1}; (*b*) it is possible to establish a one-one correspondence between α_{i+1} and α_i so that the corresponding marks are *either* homogeneous *or* coincide. In this way we construct K_{i+1}.

3) We exclude from our subsystem the remaining phonemes which do not fit into our arrangement and we draw up a new arrangement for them.

Example. We have obtained the class $K_1 = \{p, t, k\}$. By Point 2 we obtain the new classes: $K_2 = \{b, d, g\}$; $K_3 = \{p', t', k'\}$, $K_4 = \{b', d', g'\}$, $K_5 = \{c, č\}$, $K_6 = \{f, s, š, ch\}$, $K_7 = \{f', s', š'\}$, $K_8 = \{v, z, ž\}$, $K_9 = \{v', z', ž'\}$. The new arrangement is, it seems, needed for the sonants, which thus belong to another subsystem, and for j, which, it seems, forms a whole subsystem by itself.

Thus, we have obtained a division into classes within the bounds of the subsystem, each class being uniquely defined by its own archiphoneme. The set of archiphonemes α_1, α_2, ... α_i obtained by our procedure of arrangement uniquely defines a division into classes $K_1^{(1)}$, $K_2^{(1)}$ ... $K_i^{(1)}$, where the upper index indicates the number of the division and the lower index the number of the class.

4) Having selected an archiphoneme β_1, which does not coincide with any α_i considered above, and having repeated the procedure considered in Points 1-2 (Point 3 is valid only for the initial division – for the principles governing the selection of this initial division, see a little further on), we *either* exhaust all the phonemes and obtain a new division into classes each of which is defined by an archiphoneme β_i ($\beta_i \neq \alpha_j$), *or* we do not obtain a division into classes, as all the phonemes of the subsystem will not be exhausted. In the second case we consider each of the remaining phonemes as an isolated class and, at the same time, we obtain a division of the whole subsystem into classes which is defined (with precision down to the isolated classes) by the set of archiphonemes β_1, β_2, ... β_m.

5) Now we again repeat the procedure described in Point 4 and obtain a new division into classes, which is defined (with precision

down to the non-isolated classes) by the set of archiphonemes $\gamma_1, \gamma_2, \ldots \gamma_k$.

6) The procedure described in Point 5 is repeated until all archiphonemes common to at least two phonemes of the subsystem are exhausted.

We now call the number of phonemes in the given class the *capacity of the class*, and the capacity of the class most often encountered in a given division the *capacity of the division*. We shall arrange our system in various ways.

We shall agree to select the division with the greatest capacity as the initial division, the division with the next highest degree of capacity as the second one – and so on.

This condition can be fulfilled, since it is possible to go through all the possible divisions by means of the special algorithm, working in accordance with Points 1-6.

We now turn to the concept of the isolated class. It is at once clear than the following is true:

1) in the initial division there is no isolated class;
2) in each division there is at least one non-isolated class.

For instance, the second statement is true because, in the formation of the first class of the division by Points 1-2, a pair of phonemes with a common archiphoneme is always selected.

We shall call an isolated class a class of the *first kind* if, for the phoneme F which constitutes it, there exists in some non-isolated class of the division a phoneme F_1 such that F and F_1 have a common archiphoneme. Any non-isolated class and any isolated class of the first kind is called *regular*.

We now return to the idea of the subsystem in the form of a set of divisions into non-intersecting classes:

$$K_1^{(1)}, K_2^{(1)}, K_3^{(1)}, \ldots, K_n^{(1)}$$
$$K_1^{(2)}, K_2^{(2)}, K_3^{(2)}, \ldots, K_m^{(2)}$$
$$\cdots\cdots\cdots\cdots\cdots$$
$$K_1^{(l)}, K_2^{(l)}, K_3^{(l)}, \ldots, K_k^{(l)}$$

Example. We examined a division $K^{(i)}$ for the subsystem of the obstruents of Russian. We now write out this division and the other possible divisions.

$K^{(1)}$	$K^{(2)}$	$K^{(3)}$	$K^{(4)}$
$K_1^{(1)} = \{p, t, k\}$	$K_1^{(2)} = \{p, b\}$	$K_1^{(3)} = \{p, p'\}$	$K_1^{(4)} = \{t, c, s\}$
$K_2^{(1)} = \{b, g, d\}$	$K_2^{(2)} = \{t, d\}$	$K_2^{(3)} = \{b, b'\}$	$K_2^{(4)} = \{t', s'\}$
$K_3^{(1)} = \{p', t', k'\}$	$K_3^{(2)} = \{k, g\}$	$K_3^{(3)} = \{t, t'\}$	$K_3^{(4)} = \{k, ch\}$
$K_4^{(1)} = \{b' \, d', g'\}$	$K_4^{(2)} = \{b', p'\}$	$K_4^{(3)} = \{k, k'\}$	$K_4^{(4)} = \{p, f\}$
$K_5^{(1)} = \{c, č\}$	$K_5^{(2)} = \{t', d'\}$	$K_5^{(3)} = \{g, g'\}$	$K_5^{(4)} = \{b, v\}$
$K_6^{(1)} = \{f, s, š, ch\}$	$K_6^{(2)} = \{k' \, g'\}$	$K_6^{(3)} = \{f, f'\}$	$K_6^{(4)} = \{p', f'\}$
$K_7^{(1)} = \{f', s' \, š'\}$	$K_7^{(2)} = \{c\}$	$K_7^{(3)} = \{d, d'\}$	$K_7^{(4)} = \{b', v'\}$
$K_8^{(1)} = \{v, z, ž\}$	$K_8^{(2)} = \{č\}$	$K_8^{(3)} = \{s, s'\}$	$K_8^{(4)} = \{d, z\}$
$K_9^{(1)} = \{v', z', ž'\}$	*etc.*	$K_9^{(3)} = \{c\}$	$K_9^{(4)} = \{d', z'\}$
		etc.	$K_{10}^{(4)} = \{g\}$
			etc.

$K^{(1)}$ is a division of capacity 3 and this capacity is the greatest. It was for this reason that it was chosen as the initial one.

Our abstract system of arranging phonemes is convenient for formal constructions, but, because of its abstractness, it is difficult to relate it to the usual ideas of Phonology. For many readers, it seems, the following principle of arrangement may turn out to be more convenient. We consider an archiphoneme α and a maximal set of homogeneous marks $m_1, m_2, \ldots, m_t$ such that α plus any of these marks constitutes a phoneme in the given language. Now we take all the phonemes having a common archiphoneme α_1 and distinguished from one another only by the marks of the series mentioned. We carry on in this way until all the phonemes of the subsystem, united into classes by the assembly of the changeable marks, are exhausted. We shall say that this assembly of changeable marks defines a particular division, and the archiphonemes α, α_1, etc. define the classes of this division. Having chosen another maximal assembly of homogeneous marks, we obtain a new division – and so on.

Thus, in our example of the subsystem of the obstruents, the first division is defined by the assembly of the homogeneous marks of place of formation, the second division by the marks of the presence or absence of voice, the third division by the marks of hardness and softness, and, finally, the fourth division by the assembly of the homogeneous marks of the mode of formation.

It could have been shown that this principle of arrangement follows logically from the preceding one. In this connection our system allows of a whole series of interpretations well-known in Phonology.

The first of them consists of the following. Each separate division of the phonemes can be represented as a dimension (for instance, as a straight line on which the separate classes of the division appear as the points). Each phoneme is then represented as an ordered n-fold coordinate, where the ith coordinate indicates the class into which the given phoneme falls in the ith division.

In our example each phoneme is defined by four coordinates:

$$p = (K_1^{(1)}, K_1^{(2)}, K_1^{(3)}, K_4^{(4)})$$

$$b = (K_2^{(1)}, K_1^{(2)}, K_2^{(3)}, K_5^{(4)}) - \text{and so on.}$$

If this representation is extended to the whole system (adding the number of the subsystem as yet another coordinate), we obtain a representation of the phonological system in n dimensions of space close to that considered by Cherry.[12] We could even obtain a representation isomorphous with Cherry's representation if we started out from Jakobson's acoustic marks mentioned above. At the same time, as we have indicated, our subsystem would embrace the whole system. Besides, R. Jakobson's marks were chosen so that not more than two phonemes would belong to each class of any division (as in division $K^{(2)}$ and $K^{(3)}$ of our example). This allows us to talk of the mark as having exactly two values, zero and unity. This convenient concept, which has received the appellation *binariness*, is attractive by reason of its rigidness, but it is subject to criticism.[13] But, as indicated, we prefer a more traditional interpretation of marks.

This more traditional interpretation is, moreover, essential, because it allows us to connect the divisions with N. S. Trubetzkoy's classical analysis of phonological oppositions. Thus, if in a given division, no more than two phonemes belong to each class, we have a one-dimensional opposition; in the opposite case, we have a multi-dimensional opposition. The further translation of the terminology of this paragraph into N. S. Trubetzkoy's language of oppositions can easily be done by the reader himself.

§13 · *Phonological homogeneity* · *The concept of empty cells*

We now pass on to a description of the system which has been constructed. It is clear that different systems differ by the differing extent of the arrangement. From the typological point of view it is useful to have some ideally arranged system with which actual languages may be compared.

Definition. We shall say that a subsystem is *phonologically homogeneous* if, for any two divisions and for any phonemes x and y, from the condition

$$K^{(1)}(x) \cap K^{(2)}(y) \neq 0$$

(i.e. from the presence of a phoneme z which, in the division $K^{(1)}$, belongs to the same class as x, and, in the division $K^{(2)}$, belongs to the same class as y), there follows

$$K^{(1)}(y) \cap K^{(2)}(x) \neq 0.$$

It is interesting to establish the conditions under which a subsystem shows itself phonologically homogeneous. The most important condition is the absence of "empty cells". We shall say that two marks m_i and m_j are *fully homogeneous* in a given subsystem if the substitution of m_j for m_i (and m_i for m_j) in any phoneme of the given subsystem leads to a phoneme of the given subsystem. If, in a subsystem, there are two phonemes F_1 and F_2 such that F_1 is obtained from F_2 by the substitution of m_j for $m_i - m_i$ and m_j however not being fully homogeneous in the given subsystem – then we shall say that the subsystem contains an *empty cell*. Here we understand the term *empty cell* as follows: if m_i and m_j are not fully homogeneous, there exists a phoneme F such that the substitution of m_i for m_j (or m_j for m_i) leads to an empty cell, that is, the assembly of the marks does not constitute a phoneme of the given language.

Theorem 2.1.[14] If a subsystem does not contain empty cells, it is phonologically homogeneous.

With reference to the examination of the subsystem of Russian obstruents, we cannot say that it is homogeneous, because empty cells were at once established in it. But this still does not mean that the system is phonologically non-homogeneous. Our Theorem does not help to explain this, and we must turn to the analysis of particular cases. It is indeed actually possible to discover cases of non-homogeneity in it.

Consider the phoneme t. By division $K^{(4)}$ it belongs to $K_1^{(4)} = K^{(4)}(c)$, but, by division $K^{(1)}$, it belongs to $K_1^{(1)} = K^{(1)}(p)$. In other words

$$K^{(4)}(c) \cap K^{(1)}(p) = t.$$

At the same time there is no phoneme which belongs simultaneously to $K^{(4)}(p)$ and $K^{(1)}(c)$. Such a phoneme is, in general, possible; this is the affricate *pf*, as it is pronounced in the German word *Pfahl*. For Russian, instead of the phoneme *pf*, we have an empty cell associated with the fact that substitution of the mark "stopped" by the mark "affricateness" does not lead to the formation of a phoneme existing in the language.

We have seen that Theorem 2.1 only allows us to state that a certain subsystem is phonologically homogeneous; but it does not allow us to reject the homogeneity of a subsystem. In other words, it only yields a sufficient condition of homogeneity. We now need to establish some necessary conditions.

Theorem 2.2. If a subsystem is phonologically homogeneous, then two regular classes of one division cannot contain a different number of phonemes.

Corollary. A phonologically homogeneous subsystem does not contain isolated classes of the first kind.

Now we can say at once that a particular system is not phonologically homogeneous. For instance, in our example $K_6^{(1)} = \{f, s, \check{s}, ch\}$, but $K_7^{(1)} = \{f', s', \check{s}'\}$, which is sufficient for the subsystem to be phonologically non-homogeneous. The following test may also prove useful.

Theorem 2.3. If a system is phonologically homogeneous and $K^{(1)}(x)$ is an isolated class in the non-initial division $K^{(1)}$, and y belongs to the same class as x in the initial division, then $K^{(1)}(y)$ is also an isolated class.

On applying this test we see that the system in our example is not phonologically homogeneous either.

Thus $K_{10}^{(4)} = \{g\}$ is an isolated class and b belongs to the same class as g in the initial division, i.e. to $K_2^{(1)}$. But, at the same time, $K^{(4)}(b)$ is not an isolated class. From this example the presence of an empty cell is also clear, namely, the absence of a fricative, back-tongue voiced phoneme in Russian.

None of the previous tests of phonological homogeneity are, it seems, very useful in practice, as they require a preparatory arrangement of the subsystem of phonemes. We now formulate a test which is much more convenient in application, but, for this, we need one auxiliary concept.

We shall describe two phonemes as *adjacent* if it is possible to pass from one of them to the other by changing just one mark. We shall call the number of phonemes adjacent to a given phoneme the *rank* of the given phoneme in the given subsystem. We shall say that a subsystem is *full*, if any two phonemes in it can be joined by a chain in which every two phonemes occurring next to one another are adjacent.[15]

Theorem 2.4. In a phonologically homogeneous subsystem two adjacent phonemes have the same rank.

Corollary. In a full, phonologically homogeneous subsystem all phonemes have equal rank.

Thus for a full, phonologically homogeneous subsystem, it is possible to introduce the concept of the rank of the subsystem, i.e. to define this concept as a quantity coinciding with the rank of any phoneme.

We now examine one of the preceding examples. The phoneme t has the rank 6 in our subsystem (adjacent phonemes: p, k, d, t', s, c) and the phoneme p has the rank 5 (adjacent phonemes: t, k, b, p', f). This is sufficient to show that our subsystem is phonologically non-homogeneous.

It is interesting that, in Czech, the rank of the phoneme t, as in Russian, is equal to 6 (adjacent phonemes: p, k, t', d, s, c), but the rank of the phoneme p is only equal to 4 (adjacent phonemes: t, k, b, f).

This shows that the concept of rank may prove useful in the typological comparison of closely-related languages.

The concept of the fullness of a system of phonemes allows us to formulate one more important statement.

Theorem 2.5. If a subsystem is full and phonologically homogeneous, it does not contain empty cells.

In practice this statement gives us (together with Theorem 2.1) a criterion of phonological homogeneity, i.e. the absence of empty cells, for the subsystems usually considered in Phonology are full. In particular, the subsystem from our example is a full one.

The concept of homogeneity is important for the following reasons.

ML D

In every non-trivial subsystem it is possible to determine a subset of phonemes forming a phonologically homogeneous subsystem. We shall call the maximal subgroup of such phonemes the *nucleus* of the phonological subsystem.

Thus in the subsystem of our example it is possible to determine the nucleus:

$$K_1^{(1)} = \{p, t, k\} \qquad K_1^{(2)} = \{p, b\} \qquad K_1^{(3)} = \{p, p'\}$$
$$K_2^{(1)} = \{b, d, g\} \qquad K_2^{(2)} = \{t, d\} \qquad K_2^{(3)} = \{b, b'\}$$
$$K_3^{(1)} = \{p', t', k'\} \qquad K_3^{(2)} = \{k, g\} \qquad K_3^{(3)} = \{t, t'\}$$
$$K_4^{(1)} = \{b', d', g'\} \qquad K_4^{(2)} = \{b', p'\} \qquad K_4^{(3)} = \{k, k'\}$$
$$K_5^{(2)} = \{t', d'\} \qquad K_5^{(3)} = \{d, d'\}$$
$$K_6^{(2)} = \{k', g'\} \qquad K_6^{(3)} = \{g, g'\}$$

We shall say that a division is *admissible* for a given nucleus if any two phonemes belonging to the same class of it *either* both belong to the nucleus *or* both do not belong to it. So the nucleus in our example admits three divisions, $K^{(1)}$, $K^{(2)}$ and $K^{(3)}$. It can be seen that our subsystem has another nucleus consisting of the sixteen phonemes: *p, b, t, d, t', d', b', p', f, v, v', f', s, z, s', z'*. But this second nucleus (although it consists of more phonemes) admits only two divisions, $K^{(2)}$ and $K^{(3)}$.

In a subsystem we shall call the nucleus which admits the maximal number of divisions the *principal* nucleus. So the first example shows us the principal nucleus of the subsystem.

Having in mind the above interpretation of our system as an *n*-dimensional space, we shall call the number of divisions within a subsystem its *dimensionality*. The dimensionality of the subsystem and the dimensionality of the principal nucleus – and also the inter-relations between the nucleus and the whole subsystem – can serve as important typological characteristics of a language.

It appears to us that the proposed terminology may serve to exactify the question of the functional loading of the contrasts (for groups of phonemes distinguished by the most fully loaded marks go into some nucleus).

Here we are approaching the idea of constructing a model close to the one we have considered and which formalizes the approach of diachronic phonology. This idea (in somewhat different terminology) belongs to the French philologist Martinet.[16]

§14 · *Martinet's dynamic model*

Martinet considers two basic divisions of the whole set of phonemes, the division by *séries* and the division by *rows*. It is easy to present these divisions as an interpretation of our abstract divisions. It is easy to see that the division $K^{(1)}$ from our Russian example corresponds to the division by séries and that our remaining divisions correspond to the division by rows. It is easy to make sure of this if we refer to Martinet's definitions:

"On dira que des phonèmes consonantiques caractérisés par une même articulation forment une SÉRIE, si leurs autres articulations caractéristiques sont situées en différents points, le long du chenal expiratoire . . . On dira des phonèmes caractérisés par une même articulation située en un point donné du chenal expiratoire, mais distingués l'un de l'autre par quelque autre articulation distinctive, qu'ils forment un ORDRE . . .

Pour ce qui est des voyelles, il semble avantageux de baptiser 'série' l'ensemble des phonèmes caractérisés par un même type de cavité de résonance (comme, par exemple, la cavité antérieure très réduite qui caractérise les voyelles dites d'avant), mais distingués par divers degrés d'ouverture de la bouche, et 'ordre' l'ensemble des phonèmes caractérisés par le même degré d'ouverture, mais distingués par différents types de cavité de résonance."[17]

Martinet does not use the term "phonological homogeneity", but his idea corresponds completely to this concept, the more so since he uses the concept of the "empty cell" with the same meaning.

We shall try to point out the way to the formalization of Martinet's ideas in a cybernetic model.

Let the number of empty cells characterize the degree of instability, the lability, of the system, and let the subsystem have a series of conditions of equilibrium which are characterized by phonological homogeneity and can be fulfilled by the exclusion of some more or less isolated phonemes and, also, by the construction of new phonemes (owing to the fact that bound marks become relevant and variants turn into new phonemes). On the other hand, let the subsystem which is tending towards the fulfilment of phonological homogeneity be under the influence of a "perturbation" which is leading to the formation of new phonemes and new empty cells. Then each period in the development of the language will be characterized by a certain ideal model, a phonologically homogeneous system, attainable by the shortest route (i.e. by the least number of operations).

We take as an example of the working of such a model the sub-system of vowels (without diphthongs) of Modern German, as it is described by the working orthoepic norms.[18]

We determine the following assemblies by $n - 2$ marks (archi-phonemes "of the second order"):

α_1 general marks for i:, i
α_2 ,, ,, ,, y:, y
α_3 ,, ,, ,, e:, ε, ε:
α_4 ., ,, ,, $\emptyset$: , oe
α_5 ,, ,, ,, a:, a
α_6 ,, ,, ,, o:, $\mathit{\jmath}$
α_7 ,, ,, ,, u, v

These archiphonemes are selected because, within them, the marks are combined according to rules not dependent on the actual language (thus only vowels of the front series can be labial-ized). In the model we generally avoid such connections between the marks. Two pairs of marks remain: openness/closeness and length/shortness. If the marks within each pair were fully homo-geneous, we could obtain 28 vowel phonemes from the 7 archi-phonemes of the second order. In fact we have 15 phonemes. The number of empty cells is very large. However, if we determine a subsystem of 14 phonemes, excluding, for instance, ε:, then we obtain (in the assumption as to the homogeneity of archiphonemes) a certain phonologically homogeneous nucleus in which, in fact, one of the marks, for instance, length/shortness, is redundant. It is interesting that a similar process is also taking place in Modern colloquial German, where ε: and e: are beginning to fall together.[19]

An approximation to phonological homogeneity can be achieved, not only by means of changing the number of phonemes, but also by means of redefining the given system of marks. For instance, we consider the subsystem of obstruents in Czech: b, p, v, f, s, z, d, t, g, ch, k, $š$, $ž$, $č$, c, t', d' – in all 17 phonemes. If it is considered that t and t' (d and d' correspondingly) are distinguished by the mark hardness/softness, then the remaining 13 phonemes will be un-paired according to this mark, and there are 13 empty cells. If, following a series of great phonologists, we consider that t (and d) is distinguished from t' (and d') only by the mark of place of formation (*t* (*d*) contains the mark "dental" and *t'* (*d'*) the mark "front palatal"), then, as it is easy to show, the number of empty cells decreases sharply. This reasoning must, it seems, be borne in mind in characterizing the system of the consonants of Czech. From the point of view of our model it is interesting to consider, too, the controversy as to the place of the phonemes *ć*, *dź*, and also *ś* and *ź*, in the system of obstruents of Modern Polish. According to their phonetic features, the first two sounds are soft affricates and the second are soft spirants. Despite this, in the theoretical literature,[20] it is often said that the first two phonemes ought to be regarded as *t'*, *d'* and the second as *s'*, *z'*. It appears that, in the rearrangement of the Polish phonemes in which the marks are given strictly phonetically, there are more than twice as many empty cells as when the marks are redefined on the principle stated above. However, from the point of view of our model, it is of the greatest interest to examine an idea recently put forward by Stieber,[21] According to this idea *ś* (and *ź* correspondingly) in Modern Polish should be regarded as the soft correlates of *š* (*ž* correspondingly) and *s* (*z* correspondingly) at one and the same time. In terms of our model it is possible to express this idea as the maximum approximation to homogeneity, i.e. the reduction of the number of empty cells can sometimes also be achieved by way of splitting one phoneme into two (it is understood that such a splitting must be confirmed by an analysis outside the model).

These examples show that a dynamic model can be considered as a generating paradigmatic model (from given phonemes new ones are generated).

Later, we shall see that an abstract model close to the phonological one we have just examined can be suggested for Grammar too (see §30).

§15 · *Syntagmatic models*

Later, there will be mention of the relation between the phonemes established on the syntagmatic axis in the text. An excellent specimen of such a functional analysis was given by N. S. Trubetzkoy using Old Slavonic as an example.[22] For instance, Trubetzkoy suggested classifying all the consonants of this language according to what vowels could be combined with them. Thus, the consonant N was in opposition to all the remaining consonants, since only *o, ö, e, a*, occurred before it. The other consonants fell into three large classes depending on whether *either* only back vowels *or* only front vowels *or* both the one and the other were allowed before them. In the latter group, again, two subgroups were determined on the basis of the distribution – and so on.

The same method of analysis was also demonstrated by him using Ancient Greek as an example.[23] In American Descriptive Linguistics the method of syntagmatic analysis of text has been worked out most fully in the work of Bloch and Trager,[24] where the important concept of a structural unit of phonemes ("structural set") is introduced as a class of phonemes occurring in an identical environment.

We now consider a model which is constructed starting from the most simple situation, i.e. it is assumed that the text has been divided up by all possible means into pairs of sounds occurring one after another in the text. It has been observed that, to the set of ordered pairs of sounds obtained in this way, there may be appended an apparatus of the Theory of Ratios.[25]

Pairs of sounds occurring at the beginning of a word in four Slavonic languages are shown in the Table in the form of a matrix. The cross at the intersection of a row and a column indicates that, in the given language, there occurs a pair in which the sound of that particular column stands in the first place and the sound of that particular row in the second place.

The following concepts are introduced.

Degree of Fullness. We denote the set of all pairs for the given language by R. By the Degree of Fullness (D) we shall understand the ratio of the number of pairs belonging to R (we denote this by $n(R)$) to the total number of possible pairs k^2, where k is the number of sounds. Then

$$D = \frac{n(R)}{k^2}$$

For our Table this quantity equals:

Russian	Serbian	Polish	Czech
$\frac{216}{35^2} \doteq 0{\cdot}18$	$\frac{104}{25^2} \doteq 0{\cdot}17$	$\frac{213}{36^2} \doteq 0{\cdot}16$	$\frac{221}{27^2} \doteq 0{\cdot}30.$

What is interesting here is that the first three languages, with different inventories and different numbers of sounds, give an almost identical degree of fullness, whereas Czech gives a qualitatively different index.

Of course, any interpretation of these data would be premature, principally because the initial Table is not sufficiently reliable and only covers initial consonants. Nevertheless they do reflect to a certain extent the actual situation in the language. The introduction of combinations with vowels would hardly change the picture much, as the vowels in the Slavonic languages combine quite freely with all consonants.

Degree of reflexiveness. In the set of pairs of sounds we distinguish a subset of the form $\langle x, x \rangle$, i.e. such that, in its first and second places, there stand identical sounds (in the Table the crosses on the large diagonal correspond to such pairs). For the Slavonic languages the corresponding subset is very small. To it there belong:

Russian	Serbian	Polish	Czech
$\langle s, s \rangle$	0	$\langle v, v \rangle \; \langle s, s \rangle$	$\langle s, s \rangle \; \langle z, z \rangle$.

All these pairs are formed because of the productive Slavonic prefixes and they do not play an essential part. If we introduce the degree of reflexiveness as the ratio of the number of reflexive pairs $\langle x, x \rangle$ to the total number of sounds

$$P = \frac{n \langle x, x \rangle}{k},$$

then, for the Slavonic languages, this quantity is insignificant. It may be necessary for the comparison of the Slavonic languages with those where this index is large.

Such, it seems, is the position in Estonian, where it is reasonable to consider the "over-long" vowels and consonants as pairs of phonemes,[26] and where, therefore, the degree of reflexiveness is very high.

It was proposed[27] to investigate the subset of pairs possessing the properties of symmetry and transitivity in an analogous way. However, we shall not stop for these questions here.

The data as to the pairs of sounds occurring in a given language make possible the construction of an *oriented graph*, reflecting the distribution of the phonemes in the given language. And indeed each sound does represent a point on a surface. If the pair $\langle x, y \rangle$ occurred in the List, an arrow is drawn from x to y.

Consonant-pairs at the beginning

Rus-

	b	b'	c	č	d	d'	f	f'	g	g'	ch	ch'	j	k	k'	l	l'
b					+	+										+	+
b'																	
c																	
č											+						+
d																+	+
d'												+				+	
f																+	+
f'													+				
g						+										+	+
g'																	
ch																+	+
ch'																	
j																	
k																+	+
k'																	
l	+	+							+								
l'						+			+								
m			+	+					+		+	+				+	+
m'																	
n																	
n'																	
p				+		+			+							+	+
p'																	
r			+		+	+											
r'		+											+				
s	+	+	+	+	+		+	+	+		+	+	+	+	+	+	+
s'																	+
š				+							+	+	+	+	+	+	+
t													+	+	+	+	+
t'																	
v	+		+	+	+				+	+	+			+	+	+	+
v'													+				
z	+	+			+	+			+	+						+	+
z'																	
ž	+			+					+							+	
Pause	+	+	+	+	+	+	+	+	+	+	+	+	+	+	+	+	

 the Word (according to Appel)[28]

an

m	m'	n	n'	p	p'	r	r'	s	s'	š	t	t'	v	v'	z	z'	ž	vowel
						+	+									+		+
																		+
		+												+				+
+							+				+	+	+					+
	+	+				+	+						+	+		+	+	+
			+															+
						+												+
																		+
	+	+	+			+	+						+		+			+
																		+
+	+	+				+	+						+					+
																		+
																		+
+		+	+			+	+	+	+		+	+	+	+				+
																		+
																+		+
	+							+	+				+					+
	+	+				+	+	+		+				+				+
																		+
						+												+
																		+
	+	+				+	+	+	+	+	+	+						+
																		+
												+	+	+			+	+
																		+
+	+	+	+	+	+	+	+	+			+	+	+	+	+		+	+
	+	+					+					+						+
+	+	+	+	+	+	+	+				+	+	+	+				+
						+	+						+	+				+
+						+				+			+					+
+	+	+	+	+	+	+	+	+	+	+	+	+	+		+	+	+	+
																		+
	+	+	+			+	+							+				+
							+											+
			+			+	+							+				+
+	+	+	+	+	+	+	+	+	+	+	+	+	+	+	+	+	+	+

Ser-

	b	c	ć	č	d	3́	3̌	f	g	ch	j	k	l	ľ
b					+								+	+
c												+		
ć														
č												+	+	
d	+												+	
3́	+													
3̌														
f													+	
g					+								+	+
ch													+	+
j														
k			+										+	+
l														
ľ														
m													+	+
n														
ń														
p				+									+	+
r														
s		+								+	+	+	+	+
š		+	+	+								+	+	+
t												+	+	
v					+								+	
z	+		°		+				+		+		+	
ž	+				+		+		+				+	+
Pause	+	+	+	+	+	+	+	+	+	+	+	+	+	+

bian

m	n	n'	p	r	s	š	t	v	z	ž	vowel
				+							+
+				+				+			+
											+
+			+	+				+			+
+	+			+				+			+
											+
											+
				+							+
+	+	+		+				+			+
+				+			+	+			+
											+
+	+	+		+				+			+
											+
											+
	+	+		+							+
											+
											+
				+	+		+				+
											+
+	+		+	+			+	+			+
+		+	+				+	+			+
+				+				+			+
				+							+
+	+			+				+			+
+		+		+				+			+
+	+	+	+	+	+	+	+	+	+	+	+

	b	b'	c	ć	č	d	ȝ	ź	ž	f	f'	g	g'	h	ch	j	k	k'
b																		
b'																		
c																	+	
ć																		
č				+													+	
d	+															+		
ȝ	+																	
ź																		
ž												+						
f																		
f'																		
g	+					+	+											
g'																		
h																		
ch				+														
j																		
k				+														
k'																		
l												+						
ł	+											+					+	
m						+						+					+	
m'																		
n																		
n'																		
p		+		+											+			
p'																		
r						+												
s		+		+							+				+		+	
s'			+															
š'				+													+	
t															+		+	
v		+	+	+	+	+		+				+			+	+	+	
v'																		
z	+	+	+		+	+		+	+			+	+	+		+		
z'								+										
ž	+					+			+			+						
Pause	+	+	+	+	+	+	+	+	+	+	+	+	+	+	+	+	+	

h

h	l	ł	m	m'	n	n'	p	p'	r	s	s'	š	t	v	v'	z	z'	ž	vowel
+	+	+							+							+	+	+	+
																			+
+	+	+	+		+														+
		+												+	+				+
+	+	+											+	+					+
	+	+	+		+	+			+					+					+
														+					+
														+					+
															+				+
									+										+
																			+
		+	+	+	+	+			+					+	+	+	+	+	+
																			+
									+										+
		+	+						+			+		+				+	+
																			+
		+	+		+	+		+	+	+	+	+	+	+				+	+
																			+
						+					+				+			+	+
															+			+	+
		+			+	+			+		+	+						+	+
																			+
																			+
																			+
		+			+				+	+	+	+	+						+
																			+
														+	+	+		+	+
		+	+		+		+	+		+		+	+	+					+
			+		+		+	+							+				+
		+	+	+	+	+				+	+								+
		+			+						+								+
		+	+	+	+	+	+	+		+	+	+	+	+		+	+	+	+
																			+
		+	+		+	+			+	+				+			+	+	+
									+										+
		+	+	+	+				+					+	+				+
	+	+	+	+	+	+	+	+	+	+	+	+	+	+	+	+	+	+	+

Czech

	b	c	č	d'	d	ž₃	f	g	h	ch	j	k	l
b				+									+
c													+
č												+	+
d'													
d	+	+											+
ž₃	+												
f													+
g					+								+
h	+												+
ch		+											+
j					+				+				
k					+								+
l	+								+			+	
m					+				+	+		+	+
ň													
n													
p									+	+			+
r		+	+	+	+								
ř	+											+	
s	+	+	+	+	+		+	+	+	+	+	+	+
š			+									+	+
t'													
t			+							+		+	+
v	+	+	+	+	+				+	+	+	+	+
z	+	+	+	+	+		+	+	+	+	+	+	+
ž	+			+	+		+	+					+
Pause	+	+	+	+	+	+	+	+	+	+	+	+	+

m	ň	n	p	r	ř	s	š	t'	t	v	z	ž	vowel
				+	+						+	+	+
+		+	+						+	+			+
+	+		+	+				+	+				+
													+
+	+	+		+	+					+			+
													+
	+			+									+
	+	+		+									+
+	+	+		+	+					+			+
+	+	+		+	+			+		+			+
+					+								+
+	+	+		+	+	+	+		+	+			+
	+	+	+			+				+	+	+	+
	+	+		+	+	+	+				+	+	+
													+
													+
	+	+		+	+	+	+		+				+
+								+	+	+	+	+	+
									+				+
+	+	+	+	+	+	+	+		+	+	+	+	+
+	+	+	+	+				+	+	+			+
													+
+	+	+		+	+		+			+			+
+	+	+	+	+	+	+	+	+	+		+	+	+
+	+	+	+	+	+	+	+	+	+	+	+	+	+
+	+	+		+						+			+
+	+	+	+	+	+	+	+	+	+	+	+	+	+

We examine below (with some simplification) the model investigated by two Roumanian scholars, S. Marcus, the mathematician, and E. Vasiliu, the philologist.[29] Let us assume that we are given all the phonetic words of a given language in the sense of Interpretation 1. We express the word in the form of a chain of sounds. We enumerate all the sounds in every word, beginning at the end; for instance

$$f s t r e č a^{[1]}$$
$$7654321.$$

We observe that two identical sounds standing in different places will now be considered by us as different elements.

Consider a certain sound f with index i. We pick out all the pairs of form f_i, f_{i-1}, where f_i is a sound stipulated by us and f_{i-1} a sound which stands after it in at least one phonetic word.

Having carried out this operation for the whole set of sounds, we can actually construct the graph sought for.

In order that the subsequent account should be sufficiently real and linguistically meaningful, we limit ourselves to the case of the initial consonant-groups of Russian, and only consider consonant-groups beginning with v or f.

There are, for instance, the following groups with four consonants: $v_4 z_3 b_2 r_1$, $v_4 z_3 g_2 l_1$, $v_4 z_3 d_2 v_1$, $v_4 z_3 g_2 r_1$, and $f_4 s_3 kh_2 l_1$ (in writing *всхл*, e.g. *всхлипнуть*[2]).

We obtain the following subgraph

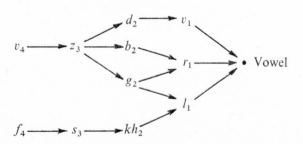

This kind of model may prove useful for the typological classification of languages, just as the analysis of empty cells did in Paradigmatics. When comparing among themselves the phonemes represented by sounds near in phonation in two different languages,

[1] meeting   [2] to sob

for instance, Russian and Polish, it is possible to enumerate the order of the corresponding junction, i.e. the number of ingoing and the number of outgoing arrows.

It is possible to use these Tables for the following purpose (leaving aside the difference between the two graphs): the number of arrows going into the given junction (Harary and Paper call this the "beta-field of phoneme *x*" in the work mentioned) corresponds to the number of crosses in the particular column, and the number of outgoing arrows (the "alpha-field of phoneme *x*") to the number of crosses in the particular row. Below we give data for sounds more or less near in pronunciation, *z, s, š*, in the four Slavonic languages and also in Roumanian (according to Marcus and Vasiliu):

Sound	Language	Number of ingoing arrows	Number of outgoing arrows
z	Russian	5	13
	Serbian	0	7
	Polish	6	22
	Czech	7	26
	Roumanian	0	8
s	Russian	5	31
	Serbian	2	13
	Polish	5	14
	Czech	8	24
	Roumanian	0	8
š	Russian	5	19
	Serbian	0	11
	Polish	6	11
	Czech	7	11
	Roumanian	0	8

Of course this material, too, is only useful for illustration, and no conclusions can be drawn from it.

In connection with this model the following interesting question arises. If we know the total number of sounds in a given chain, and also certain of these sounds, in what cases is it possible to reconstruct the remaining ones?

ML E

For example, from our sketch it is clear that, if we are given the two sounds v_4 and v_1, then the two intermediate ones can easily be reconstructed; similarly in the case that we are given v_4 and l_1. There is a more interesting case: if f_4 is given, then it is possible to reconstruct all three following ones. If we are given v_4 and r_1 we can reconstruct z_3, but we cannot reconstruct the sound following it. From the sketch it is clear why this is so. In the case when it is possible to reconstruct the intermediate sounds from two particular phonemes, one route leads from one sound to the other and back, and, when there is *one* route, then from two sounds it is possible to reconstruct the intermediate ones.[30]

§16 · *A model of generation*

Up to the present we have considered phonetic words (in the sense of the Interpretations of §9) as the initial material, and, basing ourselves on them, have then constructed the whole theory, i.e. all the models considered above have been analysing ones. Let us now see how a synthetic model may be constructed. The simplest method of construction of such a model would be the conversion of a previous model in the following sense.

Let us take a certain graph (for instance, one constructed on the basis of the data of the Table).

We shall now move from the point indicating a blank (a pause), according to the arrows of the graph, to a concluding point (if our Table had been supplemented with the combinations with vowels and consonants in the middle and end of the word, this concluding point would have been a fresh pause). We write out all the sounds through which we have passed, moving according to the graph. We obtain a succession of sounds. Moving by a second route, we obtain a second succession – and so on. In what relation to the words of the corresponding language do these chains stand?

There can here be observed an interesting lack of correspondence between the set of phonetic words analysed and the set of synthesized phonetic words. We agreed that actual words of the given language would be analysed (Interpretation 1). In other words, our graph reflected combinations which occurred in actual words of the language. But the synthesizing structure, acting in the way we have described, reveals, not only what was actually encountered in the language, but also what may be presumed potential in it.

For instance, on analysing the words *vagonovozhatyi*[1] and *glubokouvazhaemyi*[2] (with the condition that the sounds are not enumerated – and this is quite permissible, since we have enumerated them only within combinations of consonants, of which there are almost none here), we obtain (in representation by letters) the following graph:

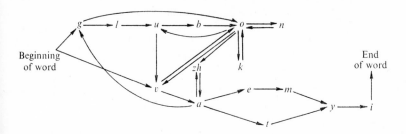

If we now realize the construction described above, it produces, not only the well-known *vagonouvazhaemyi*[3], *glubokouvazhatyi*[4], but also a whole series of other words, such as *gluvaemyi*[5], *glubovaemyi*[6], *glubonokovatyi*[7], etc.

The model generates words which have not been found in the actual text. If we take into consideration, not only the possible pairs of two elements in Russian (here for the sake of simplicity we consider the letters and not the sounds), but also the contingent probabilities of the appearance of a certain letter after a given one, then, as R. L. Dobrushin has demonstrated, it is possible to arrive at a phrase of the type *Umarano kach vsvannyi rosya nykh kovkrov nedare*[8]. Even if we take into consideration the probability of the appearance of three-letter combinations, we still obtain meaningless combinations of the type *Pokak pot durnoskaka nakonepno zne stvolovil se tvoi obnil'*. Only the taking into consideration of the probability of the appearance of four-letter combinations leads to phrases close to the "nonsense" of which mention was made in §9: *Vesel vrat'sya ne sukhom i nepo i korko*.[31]

We observe that the position would not have been essentially altered, if, instead of letters, there had been speech-sounds.[32] Meanwhile, in the four-element combinations, all the positional

---

[1] tram-driver   [2] deeply respected
[3] tram-respected   [4] deep-driver   [5-8] *nonsense*

peculiarities characteristic for the given language are already quite clearly exhibited. On the other hand, even using the probabilities of appearance of many-element (10 or more) combinations, we do not necessarily obtain phonetic words actually stipulated in the language. And this confirms the usefulness of interpreting the initial phonetic material as the set of potential phonetic words.

In conclusion, we should mention that a model analogous to that considered above constitutes the model of a language with a finite number of states which will be examined in §38.

III The basic concepts in the construction of grammatical models and their linguistic interpretation

§17 · *Morpheme or word?*

In the phonological model it was easy to take the concept of the speech-sound as the interpretation of the concept "element". In grammar the matter is not so simple. In the interpretation of the formal concept "element", it is possible to have two different units in view, namely, the morpheme and the word. The interpretation will be essentially altered, depending on the choice of this initial concept. It seems that the choice of a formally more convenient apparatus depends on this too.

We therefore now turn to the question of which unit is more convenient for formal analysis, first of all from the point of view of the criterion of determinability in the flow of speech.

In the researches of recent time, both European and American, the morpheme – in the sense of a "minimal meaningful unit" – sometimes in this meaning the term "moneme"[1] is used, and the term "morpheme" signifies only the grammatical or formal monemes – usually without a strict definition of this concept, is taken as the initial unit. It is of course obvious that the morpheme is a unit of language, but in speech there appear separate representatives of morphemes, or *allomorphs*, which it is convenient to call "morphs". For instance the morphs *vod, vot, vad* (cf. *vody*[1], *vod*[2], *voda*[3]) appear as allomorphs of one morpheme as a unit of language.

A series of formal procedures for determining morphs has been worked out (we shall pause to examine some of them later). However all these procedures are still too complicated – and the main thing is, they are not sufficiently precise for the concept "morpheme", which is by no means so obvious as the concept "word", to be taken as the initial one.

The choice of the morpheme as the initial unit is complicated by

[1] waters   [2] *do., gen. pl.*   [3] water

the following circumstance. As is well-known, morphs are connected together in different ways within words or speech-tacts. As we show below, in many languages, some groups of morphemes (endings, in part suffixes) are more closely connected to the stem than others (prefixes, components of compound words). In connection with this, the determining of morphemes by any effective procedure without reference to meaning is extremely difficult.

But *segmentation* – the dismemberment of the speech-flow – should be carried out on the basis of clear formal criteria. We now intend to show that some units, which are, for a number of languages, near to the word (in the sense "word-form"), but, in general, occupy a position intermediate between the morph and the word, can be distinguished on the basis of two fairly simple formal criteria, a phonological one and a constructive one.

§18 · *The phonological criterion of segmentation*

As N. S. Trubetzkoy[2] has shown, there is a series of phonological signals which indicates the boundaries of words or morphemes. These boundary-signals ("Grenzsignale") can be unitary or group signals. Examples of unitary signals are provided by the glottal stop in German, in the south Polish dialects, in some Czech dialects, in Armenian and in other languages; by the fixed accent in German, Czech, Armenian, Polish and other languages; by the occurrence of special positional variants of phonemes, for instance, by aspirated p', t', k' in the root-morphemes of German. Group-signals are special combinations of sounds, for instance, in German or Estonian the combination *consonant* $+ h$ (for other examples see the work of N. S. Trubetzkoy already mentioned).

Pauses are also a very important boundary-signal.

We shall now assume that we have been given all the boundary-signals, or at least the most important of them, for the language under investigation in the form of a list. Of course, some of the signals enumerated above were obtained on the basis of a knowledge of the boundaries of words. However, at first, we could have confined ourselves to those for whose obtaining no preliminary knowledge of the dismemberment of text is required (for instance, pauses, and information obtained on the basis of an analysis of the distribution of pauses). Secondly (and this, it seems, is the most important), the assumption that we have a list of phonological boundary-signals in no way violates the strictness of the exposition, for it does not lead to any false conclusions later on.

It is clear, however, that the phonological criterion alone is not sufficient, for in many languages, for instance in French, the boundaries between words or morphemes in general, and as a rule, are not indicated; and in other languages these boundaries are by no means indicated in all cases.

Therefore it is essential to take into consideration yet another criterion of segmentation.

§19 · *The constructive criterion of segmentation*

We shall say that a *boundary runs* between the two phonemes x and y, if it is possible to omit the part of the phrase including x, or the part including y, without changing the grammatical correctness of the phrase. For instance, in the phrase *on segodnya perestaralsya*[1], it is possible to draw the following boundaries: *on / segodnya / pere / staralsya*. In the German phrase *der Täter verachtet diese Verordnung* the boundaries run in the following way: *der / Täter / ver / achtet / diese / Ver / ordnung* (cf. in Russian *prestupnik / preziraet / eto / prikazanie*).

In different languages these criteria are connected together in different ways. But usually – and this is one of those surprising linguistic phenomena which still need explanation – the phonological criterion is confirmed by the constructive one, and vice versa. We quote examples.

In Russian and other Slavonic languages the presence of a boundary (according to our constructive criterion) within a word is a very rare phenomenon; prefixes are usually closely welded to the stem, cf. the common phenomenon of parasynthesis of the type *naplyasat'sya*[2], *poberezh'e*[3], *podokonnik*[4], *predserdie*[5]. At the same time, there is a group of phonemes welded together by a whole series of phonetic marks, a unit, in which, as A. A. Reformatskii so neatly puts it, the basic laws of positional change are brought into

---

[1] He / today / overdid [it]. [2] to be exhausted
[3] shore [4] window-sill [5] auricle

action – and this is the word or, even, a more extensive formation, i.e. the speech-tact.[3] The parts of the word are still more closely welded together in the Romance languages.

On the other hand, in German and other Germanic languages, the presence of boundaries within the word is a very frequent phenomenon.[4] It is enough to recall compound words of German of the type *Arbeitsamt, Welthandel*, etc. in which it is easy to determine the boundary by the constructive criterion.

This boundary coincides very frequently with the phonological one. Thus, in our examples, the glottal stop occurs on the boundary, e.g. *fɛr'axtən, fɛr'ɔrdnuŋ, 'arbaets'amt*, as also do aspirated *t*, cf. *t'aeter* and the combination *consonant + h*, e.g. *vɛlthandəl*. Sometimes a very important phonological boundary criterion, such as a pause, appears between the elements of a compound word, cf. Schiller in "Wallenstein":

> Jetzt muss
> Gehandelt werden, schleunig, eh die *Glücks*
> *-Gestalt* mir wieder wegfliegt überm Haupt.

The compound word *Glücksgestalt* is rendered separate by the phenomenon of "enjambment".

In German, there is thus to be observed a marked difference between endings and suffixes on the one hand and between components of compound words and prefixes on the other; the first are not marked off either by the phonological or the constructive criterion, whereas the second are easily distinguished. In this respect German does not in any way constitute an exception. There is an analogous situation in many Finno-Ugrian languages, and, in particular, in Finnish or Hungarian, where the action of vowel-harmony as a rule extends to the ending, but does not extend to any other component of a compound word; for instance, Finnish *käsikirjoitus* 'manuscript' consists of a part with front vocalism *käsi* and a part with back vocalism *kirjoitus*; at the same time the suffix has the same vocalism as the second component.

§20 · *The basic speech-units*

As we have already shown, the determination of morphs is a very complicated affair. It should be noted that, in order to draw constructive and phonological boundaries, there is no need, generally speaking, for any information about morphemes; we did not use this term in defining boundaries, but only in explaining the examples. Therefore it is possible to determine the basic units which are being submitted to analysis without reference to the concept of the morpheme.

We shall say that a continuous succession of phonemes in a grammatically correct phrase constitutes a *minimal segment* if it occurs between the two nearest boundaries determined by the constructive criterion.

If the boundary of a minimal segment corresponds to some phonological boundary, i.e. if its beginning and end coincide with a phonological boundary-signal, then we call this minimal segment *phonologically correct*.

Definition. The basic speech-unit (abbreviation: BSU) is:

1) any phonologically correct minimal segment;

2) any succession of phonemes having the same distribution as i.e. occurring in the same environments (cf. §23) as a certain BSU, and not decomposable into other BSU's;

3) any succession of phonemes which lies between the two nearest BSU's.

As can easily be observed, this definition is constructed recursively, i.e. it takes us back every time to a certain initial step – but it seems that it is precisely in this way that we should form constructive linguistic definitions.[5] (In constructing this definition the author based himself on certain ideas put forward verbally by P. S. Kuznetsov.)

It is easy to confirm that, for Russian and other Slavonic languages (as distinct, for instance, from German or Estonian), the BSU, as a rule, coincides with what is usually understood as "the word in speech", or "the word-form". Since the determination of the BSU in speech is, as we see, subordinate to very simple conditions, and the BSU in practice coincides with the word, we shall, in what follows, operate with the concept of the word (this term is much more useful for linguistic interpretation than the BSU), and we shall use the concept of the morpheme only as a derivative, when we show that a partition into morphemes can be obtained starting from a partition into words.

Thus, in interpreting the model, we shall take the word as the initial element (the word in speech, or the "word-form"). This choice can be supported by the following consideration. As we have shown in §6, it is essential to take into consideration the connections between making models and the statistical analysis of Language. In particular, it is appropriate to construct the model so that, based on it, there may be constructed a probability-model, which may then be interpreted fruitfully. So, in the choice of the unit, it is essential to bear the following circumstance in mind. In Linguistic Statistics, the most interesting research has proved to be that in which the word has been taken as the initial unit ("from blank to blank"). It was for words in this sense that Zipf's remarkable law was discovered:

$$f_r = K.r^{-\gamma}$$

where r is the rank of the word, i.e. its number in a list arranged according to decreasing frequency, f_r is the frequency of the word of rank r, K and γ are certain parameters.[6]

It is clear that, in statistical researches too, an impulsion towards the choice of the word as unit has been its distinctiveness, but the significance of the results obtained represents, all the same, a supplementary argument in favour of the choice of the word as the initial unit.

It does not however follow that it should be thought that, in the interpretation of models, it is, in general, possible to dispense with morphemic analysis, i.e. the drawing of boundaries within word-forms. We are dealing only with a succession of operations. We have chosen a course in which the word is taken as the initial concept, and the principles of morphemic analysis are discussed on the basis of words. In some works (for instance, in Greenberg) a different course is chosen: at the beginning, the morpheme is defined on the basis of the analysis of phrases and then the word is defined.

The strict determination of boundaries within the word-form is extremely important from the typological point of view too. The fact is that, up to now, all the typological classifications suggested, including the most thorough of them, that due to Sapir,[7] start out, essentially, from the dismemberment of words into parts: root, derivational formants, flexions. Recently, Greenberg suggested an interesting modification of Sapir's scheme which allows us to make use of quantitative indices in the comparison of texts in different languages. As follows:

1) degree of syntheticity:

$$\text{the ratio:} \quad \frac{\text{number of morphemes}}{\text{number of words}};$$

2) degree of agglutination:

$$\text{the ratio:} \quad \frac{\text{number of words with at least one boundary}}{\text{number of boundaries}};$$

3) degree of compactness ("compounding"):

$$\text{the ratio:} \quad \frac{\text{number of root-morphemes}}{\text{number of words}};$$

4) degree of derivation:

$$\text{the ratio:} \quad \frac{\text{number of derivational formants}}{\text{number of words}};$$

5) degree of flexionality:

$$\text{the ratio:} \quad \frac{\text{number of flexions}}{\text{number of words}};$$

6) degree of prefixation:

$$\text{the ratio:} \quad \frac{\text{number of prefixes}}{\text{number of words}};$$

7) degree of suffixation:

$$\text{the ratio:} \quad \frac{\text{number of suffixes}}{\text{number of words}};$$

– and some others.

The Table on page 56, which represents a somewhat abbreviated version of Greenberg's,[8] shows how interesting are these indices (obtained, admittedly, from comparatively short texts).

It is clear, however, that the successful realization of Greenberg's method entirely depends on the presence of strict criteria for the determination of the units. Later, some models which allow us to make a more precise segmentation of the word-forms will be in-

Index	Sanskrit	Anglo-Saxon	Persian	English	Yakut	Swahili	Vietnamese
Syntheticity	2·59	2·12	1·52	1·68	2·17	2·55	1·06
Agglutination	0·09	0·11	0·34	0·30	0·51	0·67	0
Compactness	1·13	1·00	1·03	1·00	1·02	1·00	1·07
Derivation	0·62	0·20	0·10	0·15	0·35	0·07	0
Flexionality	0·84	0·90	0·39	0·53	0·82	0·80	0
Prefixation	0·16	0·06	0·01	0·04	0	1·16	0
Suffixation	1·18	1·03	0·49	0·64	1·15	0·41	0

vestigated. Meanwhile we may note that one may well add the ratio

$$\frac{\text{number of BSU's}}{\text{number of word-forms}}$$ to Greenberg's indices.

As we have seen, BSU's can be determined fairly objectively. Since this index is close to unity for a whole series of languages, for instance, for the Slavonic languages, it would seem that the introduction of the BSU for typology, in the sense that Greenberg suggested, is not essential. However it is possible to substitute "the number of BSU's" for "the number of words" in all Greenberg's indices. It would seem that sufficiently objective indices, which are also interesting from the point of view of typology, will be obtained in this case.

§21 · *The concept of the registered phrase*

In the preceding exposition we have several times made use of the concept of the phrase. In Linguistics, the term "phrase" is used with more than one meaning. The following is, however, important for us. Those philologists who distinguished the terms "phrase" and "sentence" invested the term "phrase" with a much wider sense. The definition of S. Karcevskij is especially important from this point of view: "La phrase est une unité de communication actualisée. Elle n'a pas de structure grammaticale propre. Mais elle possède une structure phonique particulière qui est son *intonation*. C'est précisément l'intonation qui fait la phrase. N'importe quel mot ou assemblage de mots, n'importe quelle forme grammaticale, n'importe quelle interjection peuvent, si la situation l'exige, servir d'unité de communication".[9]

We now consider how the "phrase" in this sense is reflected in the written text – and this will be the subject of investigation in the next part of the present work. Intonation is hardly reflected in text (except for some marks of punctuation). This leaves any combination of words independent of their grammatical formation. We can thus see that the "phrase" may well serve as an interpretation of the concept "sequence" (see §2) on the level where the words appear as units. Thus, a phrase is any ordered succession of words.

Note. It is clear that proceeding from the intonational structure of the phrase is only an abstraction. However, it is possible to imagine that, in the analysis of actual languages, one more abstract word, made up of a succession of the so-called suprasegmental symbols, is attributed to each phrase. For instance, the English phrase *I'm going home* can be taken down as: *I'm going home* $+231\search$, where 2 is the high tone, 3 the middle one and 1 the very high tone, and the sign $\searcw$ is the concluder of the sentence ("clause terminal"). Given such an approach, all the subsequent apparatus may, it seems, also be used for cases in which the intonational structure of the phrase comes under investigation. In particular, for the models considered in Chapter V, a set of symbols is provided which allows us to obtain a reflexion of the transformation of the intonational structures too.[10]

It is clear that our acceptance of the term "phrase" will be linked with certain psychological difficulties which need to be overcome for a better understanding of what follows. In particular, we shall regard as phrases, not only such nonsensical (though grammatical) constructions, as

1) *kentavr vypil kruglyi kvadrat*[1];[11]

2) *ideya yarostno spit*[2];

but also such successions as

3) *splyu ideya yarostno*[3];

4) *prishel s*[4].

It is clear that all phrases (in this sense) fall into two groups: those constructed correctly and those constructed incorrectly. Chomsky,[12] from whom some of the examples quoted are borrowed, put forward the following criterion for the correct construction of a phrase: Phrases 1 and 2 are pronounced with the normal intonation of the narrative sentence, whereas 3 or 4 cannot be pronounced with such an intonation.

Thus Chomsky virtually goes back to Karcevskij's criterion. This is significant, but, in a certain sense, constricts the interpretations

[1] [The] centaur / drank up / [a] round / square.   [2] [The] idea / furiously / sleeps.   [3] [I] sleep / [the] idea / furiously.   [4] [He] came / with.

of our models. It is not clear why it is necessary to reject in advance such a completely meaningful interpretation of the sequences given us as "extracts from text, actually encountered in text". This is the more important since the situation examined in Descriptive Linguistics will be partially modelled in the two succeeding chapters. In the meantime the term "phrase" will often be used here in the sense of "an utterance or part of an utterance bounded by successive pauses".[13] In Descriptive Linguistics an "utterance" is understood as being any segment of text, and the only source of data for the philologist is the set of utterances, which Harris calls the "universe of discourse" (see §3). This only includes the phrases actually encountered by the investigator, i.e. a finite set of phrases. Later we see (§43) that a similar interpretation is useful in resolving some logical questions. We shall deal with this by two interpretations of the concept "registered phrase":

Interpretation 1. The set of registered phrases is the set of all phrases actually occurring in a sufficiently long text in the language being investigated (cf. Interpretation 1 of the concept "phonetic word" in §9).

Interpretation 2. The set of registered phrases is the set of grammatically correct phrases in the language being investigated, or – what apparently is the same – the set of potentially possible phrases of the given language (cf. Interpretation 2 of the concept "phonetic word" in §9).

From now on, Interpretation 2 will be the basic one. Since, however, the concept of grammatical correctness is intuitive, we shall consider that the criterion of registration lies outside the formal system. One could conceive the matter as follows: we have an "oracle" to which we can turn to verify whether a certain phrase is registered.

§22 · *The concept of the B-structure of phrases*

Later we shall examine all possible divisions of the set of initial elements, i.e. words (word-forms), into non-intersecting classes. We encounter such classes in any grammatical theory. It is possible to imagine that all words have been divided into the classes of nouns, adjectives, verbs, etc., or, on the other hand, that all words have been divided into classes according to their endings, or, for instance, according to the type of stem (as is usual for the ancient Indo-European languages) – and so on.

An interesting classification of the classes and subclasses of words arising in Linguistics has been suggested by A. A. Kholodovich.[14] At the moment, however, we are not interested in the criterion for division into classes. The only important thing is that, by some criterion, all words are divided into non-intersecting classes.

With each phrase in the language being investigated there can now be coordinated a chain of classes of the division we have adopted. For instance, if we are given a division into a class of nouns (S), a class of adjectives (A), a class of prepositions (Pr), a class of verbs (V) and a class of remaining words (Z), then, for instance, to the registered phrase:

Malen'kii mal'chik ne vidit menya i devochki[1],

there corresponds the chain of classes:

A S Z V Z Z S.

An unregistered phrase might, however, also correspond to this chain of classes, for instance:

Krasnuyu slon khotya begat' menya no sobak[2].

Finally, it is possible to devise a chain of classes to which not a single registered phrase corresponds, for instance:

Pr Pr Pr Z Pr.

We now consider the situation arising in an abstract division B. Let the given phrase be $A = x_1 x_2 \ldots x_n$.

In the given division B, establish a correspondence between each word x_i and the class $B(x_i)$. In other words, we construct the mapping of the set of words onto the set of classes. The chain of classes $B(x_1)B(x_2) \ldots B(x_n)$ corresponding to the given phrase A in the given division B will be called the *B-structure of phrase A*, and will be denoted by B(A). The B-structure is called *registered* if at least one phrase corresponding to the structure is registered.[15]

A B-structure is called *complete*[16] if any phrase corresponding to the structure is registered.

[1] [The] little / boy / not / sees / me / and / [the] girl.
[2] [The] red / elephant / although / [to] run / me / but / dog

Note. The use of the term "structure" in the sense of a chain of sets at first sight contradicts the accepted use of words in Linguistics. But the word "structure" is so frequently used nowadays that it has ceased to yield any information at all. Therefore it is quite permissible to attribute to it the meaning it had during the period of the formulation of modern Linguistics and modern Logic. Our usage of the term "structure", taken from O. S. Kulagina, fully corresponds to the use of this term in the following statement: "Die scharfsinnige Logistik unserer Zeit kennt und verwendet in ihrem Bereiche mit bestem Erfolge den 'Strukturbegriff'; es ist ohne weiteres möglich, an einem schlichten lateinischen Satze wie *Caius amavit Camillam* die Abstraktion zu vollziehen, welche das Strukturelle im Sinne der Logistik erkennen lässt; ich schreibe *-us, -avit, -am* und denke mir die Leerstellen erfüllbar durch andere Wörter je einer bestimmten Klasse".[17]

§23 · *The concept of equivalence*

Despite all the differences that exist between the separate Schools in modern Linguistics, there is one thing that unites all their tendencies, namely, the method of distributive analysis,[18] which consists in exhibiting classes of elements which are interchangeable in some sense or other. The procedure for verifying the interchangeability, known in the Copenhagen School as "the test of commutation", and in Descriptive Linguistics as "substitution", is, it seems, one of the basic instruments of investigation in modern Linguistics. This takes on a special significance in Descriptive Linguistics, particularly for those persons representing it who leave meaning entirely out of consideration and reduce all linguistic structure to the distribution of phonemes and morphemes.[19] It is, however, expedient not to connect the activity of the representatives of this school of thought with their views on the main point, boundaries and general methods of linguistic investigation, and to attach the term "Descriptive Linguistics" to that part of the Science of Language which deals with the analysis of the relations between certain linguistic objects[20] on the basis of an analysis of their distribution, i.e. by making use of the methods of substitution.

It is interesting that the tradition which stems from the antique grammars, and which has been scorned in theoretical courses of syntax, that of putting questions of the type "*Kto* sidit v komnate?"[1] in order to discover the subject, is, in fact – with a correct understanding of the root of the matter, which has long been lost sight of in Grammar – very close to the ideas of distributive analysis.

[1] Who / is sitting / in / [the] room?

As A. M. Peshkovskii remarks, questions are "one of the forms of the substitution of one set of words for another in word-combinations"[1].[21] There is determined a class of words equivalent in that all of them are able to take the place of the dots in the phrase "... sidit v komnate".

Similarly, the corresponding tradition in Logic stems from the Aristotelian teaching on categories.[22] And, here, one of the lines of development led to Husserl's[23] "semantic category" (*Bedeutungskategorie*), that is, to the concept of a class of words, or of groups of words, such that the replacement of one set of elements of the same class by others does not lead to the nonsensifying of the whole context. This concept received a further exactifying in Ajdukiewicz's work on syntactic connectivity.[24]

An analysis of the problems of synonymy in actual and artificial languages led Carnap[25] to the concept of the "extensional" of any predicate, that is, to the assembly of objects to which the given predicate may be applied. Two predicates have an identical extensional if they are applied to identical objects. From the linguistic point of view we are dealing with the analysis of all possible phrases of a certain stipulated language in which there occur the predicates P and Q.

These remarks show that the significance of the idea of equivalence goes far beyond the bounds of strictly descriptive analysis. We start, however, with those concepts which are used in Descriptive Linguistics. We shall consider that two words x and y belong to one class with respect to a given context, or, more concisely, to one "contextual class", if two registered phrases have been encountered in which x and y occurred in an identical environment. For instance, in Russian, the words *slona*[2], *dom*[3], *seledku*[4], belong to one contextual class, since all of them occur in the phrase "*ya vizhu* ..."[5]. It is clear that every word goes into several contextual classes.

The concept of the contextual class is interesting in that it apparently allows one to pass from Interpretation 1 of the set of registered phrases to Interpretation 2 (i.e. the interpretation of the set of registered phrases as correctly constructed, or as potential phrases).

Let us assume that we are given phrases actually encountered, i.e. registered according to Interpretation 1. Then we can suggest the

[1] [Translation – *N.F.C.O. and A.S.C.R.*]
[2] elephant   [3] house   [4] herring   [5] I / see.

following definition of the correctly constructed, or of the potential, phrase. We shall consider that a phrase is correctly constructed if it is registered according to Interpretation 1, or obtained from a correctly constructed phrase by means of the substitution of one word x by a word belonging to one of the contextual classes to which x belongs.

We show, for instance, that the phrase *Ideya yarostno spit*[1] is correctly constructed. In fact the phrase *Devochka spokoino spit*[2] has been registered according to Interpretation 1 and is therefore correctly constructed (the first condition in our definition).

The words *ravnodushno*[3] and *spokoino* belong to one contextual class (by the context "*on . . . skazal*"[4]), the words *ravnodushno* and *yarostno* belong to one contextual class (by the context ". . . *vzglyanut'* "[5]), cf. the examples quoted in S. I. Ozhegov, *Slovar' russkogo yazyka* s.v. *vzglyanut'*. The words *devochka* and *ideya* belong to one class (by the context "*shchastlivaya . . .*"[6], cf. *shchastlivaya ideya* in D. N. Ushakov, *Tolkovyi slovar' russkogo yazyka*).

We obtain the succession of phrases:

> *Devochka spokoino spit,*
> *Devochka ravnodushno spit,*
> *Devochka yarostno spit,*
> *Ideya yarostno spit,*

and all the phrases, including the last one, are correctly constructed.

This construction reminds one very much of the transition from Interpretation 1 of the phonetic word to Interpretation 2 (see §9), and in this lies its fundamental interest.

However, contextual classes are unsuitable for operations within the model (for which the set of registered phrases is given from without), since, first, these classes intersect for the various contexts and, secondly, some accidental words may belong to these classes; for instance *khorosho*[7] belongs to the same contextual class as *slona*[8], *stol*[9], *seledku*[10] (by the context "*ya vizhu . . .*"[11]). Therefore, in the models which we are considering, the concept of interchangeability will be formulated in such a way that it has divided all words into non-intersecting classes.

---

[1] [The] idea / furiously / sleeps. [2] [The] girl / peacefully / sleeps.
[3] indifferently [4] He . . . / said. [5] to look
[6] happy [7] well [8] elephant
[9] table [10] herring [11] I / see.

The following definition of equivalence fulfils this requirement. We shall say that the element x_i is *E-equivalent* to the element x_j (denoted by $x_i \underset{E}{\sim} x_j$) if (1) for any registered phrase of the form $A_1 x_i A_2$, the phrase $A_1 x_j A_2$ is also registered, and (2) for any registered phrase $B_1 x_j B_2$, the phrase $B_1 x_i B_2$ is also registered (A_1, A_2, B_1 and B_2 are arbitrary phrases).[26]

In this form, the definition of equivalence was formulated by V. A. Uspenskii.[27] O. S. Kulagina's formulation follows somewhat different lines: $x \underset{E}{\sim} y$ if, for any phrases A and B, phrases of the form AxB and AyB are simultaneously registered or simultaneously not registered. It is clear that the two formulations are equivalent and, in what follows, we sometimes use one, sometimes the other.

E-equivalence possesses the following properties:

1) *reflexiveness*: $x \underset{E}{\sim} x$ (for any registered phrase $A_1 x A_2$ the phrase $A_1 x A_2$ is registered);

2) *symmetry*: if $x \underset{E}{\sim} y$, then $y \underset{E}{\sim} x$ (this symmetry stems from the symmetry of the first and second conditions);

3) *transitivity*: if $x \underset{E}{\sim} y$ and $y \underset{E}{\sim} z$, then $x \underset{E}{\sim} z$ (if $A_1 x A_2$ is registered, then $A_1 y A_2$ is registered; if $A_1 y A_2$ is registered, then $A_1 z A_2$ is registered; that is, if $A_1 x A_2$ is registered, then $A_1 z A_2$ is registered; in exactly the same way it is shown that, from the registration of $B_1 z B_2$, there follows the registration of $B_1 x B_2$).

The whole set of words is divided into a series of non-intersecting subsets which we shall call *families* (S_1, S_2 ... S_n).

If, in Russian, the set of registered phrases is interpreted as the set of correctly constructed phrases, we obtain the following examples of families:

S_1 – *stolu*[1], *oknu*[2], *cheloveku*[3], *klopu*[4], *duraleyu*[5] ...
S_2 – *khokhotal*[6], *prygal*[7], *begal*[8], *vizzhal*[9] ...
S_3 – *khorosho*[10], *plokho*[11], *somnitel'no*[12] ...
S_4 – *kogda*[13], *gde*[14], *kak*[15] ...

To every phrase it is now possible to juxtapose a succession of sequences such that a definite family corresponds to each element.

[1] table	[2] window	[3] man	[4] bug	[5] fool (*1-5 dat. sg.*).
[6] laughed	[7] jumped	[8] ran	[9] whistled	[10] well
[11] badly	[12] doubtfully	[13] when	[14] where	[15] how.

We call such a succession the *S-structure of the phrase A* and denote it by S(A).

Phrase	*Professor*	*voshel*	*v*	*auditoriyu*[1]
S-structure	*Professor* *slon*[2] *chelovek*[6] *storozh*[9] *predok*[12] etc.	*voshel* *prygnul*[3] *dvinulsya*[7] *priekhal*[10] etc.	*v* *na*[4] etc.	*auditoriyu* *komnatu*[5] *kukhnyu*[8] *zvezdu*[11] *kometu*[13] *raketu*[14] etc.

The concept of the S-structure reminds one very much of the celebrated example constructed by L. V. Shcherba: *Glokaya kuzdra shtenno budganula bokra i kudlyavit bokrenka.* This is not a phrase of the Russian language, for not one of the words is a word of Russian. But it can, in a certain sense, be regarded as an S-structure: *glokaya* – as the name of a family of adjectives in *-aya*, all equivalent one to the other: *krasivaya*[15], *bol'shaya*[16], *glubokaya*[17], *pestraya*[18], etc.; *kuzdra* – as the name of a family of feminine singular nouns, all equivalent one to the other: *slonikha*[19], *strekoza*[20], *korova*[21], *mamasha*[22], etc.; *shtenno* – as the name of a family of adverbs of manner: *khorosho*[23], *plokho*[24], *sil'no*[25], *slabo*[26], etc.; *budganula* – as the name of a family of verbs of type *kol'nula*[27], *ushchipnula*[28], *podkovyrnula*[29], etc. The S-structure "*Glokaya kuzdra . . .*" is, of course, registered, for there is, for instance, in Russian, the phrase: *Gruznaya slonikha lovko podtolknula slona i laskaet slonenka*[30], which is registered.

The examples quoted may lead to the formation of a false impression, namely, that the family corresponds to a class of words with fixed form. In general, this is far from being the case. For instance, the nouns of Indonesian, which are in no way different from one another in their formation, fall into families such as:

[1] [The] professor / went / into / [the] lecture-room.   [2] elephant   [3] jumped   [4] onto   [5] room   [6] man   [7] moved   [8] kitchen   [9] watchman   [10] arrived   [11] star   [12] ancestor   [13] comet   [14] rocket   [15] beautiful   [16] big   [17] deep   [18] variegated   [19] she-elephant   [20] dragon-fly   [21] cow   [22] mother   [23] well   [24] badly   [25] strongly   [26] weakly   [27] pierced   [28] pinched   [29] uttered biting remarks   [30] [The] massive / she-elephant adroitly / has pushed / [the] elephant / and / is caressing / [the] elephant-calf.

S$_1$ – *mahasiswa*	'student'	*dewi*	'goddess'
murid	'pupil'		
S$_2$ – *harimau*	'tiger'	*manuk*	'hen'
kuda	'horse'		
S$_3$ – *rumah*	'house'	*pisang*	'banana'
buku	'book'		
S$_4$ – *surat*	'letter'	*bedil*	'gun', etc.

In this language, the grouping into families is connected with the so-called "counting" words. Words from S$_1$ are those which can stand after the counting word *orang* 'man', words from S$_2$ stand after the counting word *ekor* 'tail', words from S$_3$ after the counting word *buah* 'fruit' and words from S$_4$ after the word *putjuk* 'shoot'. We are dealing with grammatical not semantic groupings, since the corresponding counting words have to be used after every numeral, for instance:

saja	*membeli*	*manuk*	*tiga*	*ekor*
'I'	'bought'	'hen'	'three'	'tail'.

In other languages, for instance in Swahili, similar – at first sight semantic – groupings into families are formed morphologically also. Thus, for Swahili, the family corresponds to the grammatical class.

The distribution by families is not connected with the formation of the word, although in a series of languages, for instance, the Slavonic languages, it is also accompanied by definite morphological indices. It is connected with the syntactic properties of the word and depends on the kind of (grammatical) contexts in which the given word is used. Here lies the value of the concept "family", which can be applied to the analysis of arbitrary languages independently of the morphological technique which characterizes languages of a definite type.

We observe now that another approach to the concept of the family is also possible, one leading to the same results. Instead of the equivalence of words, it is possible to consider the equivalence of *environments* and to determine a class of equivalent environments for a word. This idea was used by A. N. Kolmogorov in constructing the formal analogue of "case".

Kolmogorov's definition of Case is clear in V. A. Uspenskii's exposition.[28] In this exposition the initial concepts of "object" and "state", which cannot be defined in the terms introduced in §20 and §21, are used.

We shall try to explain the idea of the definition without going outside what can be formulated in our initial terms.

We call a registered phrase in which one word has been replaced by dots a "phrase with dots" (R. L. Dobrushin).

Two phrases with dots are called equivalent with respect to a word x, if, in both, x can be substituted for the dots so that the phrase obtained will be registered. For instance, in Russian, the phrases with dots "... *kipit*"[1] and "*koshka p'et* ..."[2] are equivalent with respect to the word *moloko*[3]. These phrases with dots are not however equivalent with respect to the word *voda*[4]. In connection with this we introduce a new definition. Two phrases with dots are *absolutely equivalent* if they are equivalent with respect to any word which, on being put into at least one of the two phrases with dots, makes the phrase registered. For instance, the phrases with dots "*koshka p'et* ...", "*koshka lyubit* ..."[5], "*ya vizhu* ..."[6] are absolutely equivalent. The absolute equivalence of two phrases with dots possesses the properties of symmetry, reflexiveness and transitivity. The set of phrases with dots is divided into non-intersecting classes. A. N. Kolmogorov suggested calling these classes "cases".

It is easy to see that these classes correspond to families. In §34 we shall see that the correspondence between the cases and the families is quite complicated. But the actual idea of the definition of the traditional linguistic categories in terms of equivalence has proved extremely fruitful (as we shall see in Chapter IV).

We now generalize the concept of equivalence into arbitrary B-structures.

We shall consider that the element B_i (in a given division B) is B-equivalent to the element B_j (and we write this $B_i \underset{B}{\sim} B_j$), if, for any registered structure of form $B(A_1)B_iB(A_2)$, the structure $B(A_1)B_jB(A_2)$ is registered, and, for any registered structure $B(D_1)B_jB(D_2)$, the structure $B(D_1)B_iB(D_2)$ is registered.

If we compare this definition with the definition of E-equivalence, we see that, there, we were simply dealing with a particular case of B-division, namely one in which each class consists of just one word; we shall call such a division a *unitary* one.

---

[1] is boiling   [2] [The] cat / is drinking.   [3] milk
[4] water   [5] [the] cat / loves.   [6] I / see.

§24 · *The concept of the environment*

The concept of the environment will be used in a whole series of models. We shall consider that, besides the initial units and certain registered sequences, we are given a division into non-intersecting classes which we shall call *environments*; that is, for every element x, it is known to which environment $\Gamma(x)$ it belongs.

First of all there arises the question why a need for a new initial concept which has no analogue in phonological models arises in grammatical models. This is connected with one cardinal difference between Grammar and Phonology, which, as is well-known, is the following: the latter deals only with the *plane of expression* in Language, i.e. with a certain assembly of formal signals, whereas, in Grammar, we cannot wholly disregard the *plane of content*, i.e. we must take into consideration not only the signifier but also the signified.

On the other hand, it is clear that, in the model, the plane of content should be reflected in a strictly formal way, as something given. This is achieved by the establishment of environments.

The fact that two words (BSU's) belong to one environment reflects the fact that they carry identical semantic information. The latter, however, is not very exact, and we therefore explain later on by examples what interpretations can usefully be given to the concept of the environment.

The basic interpretation of the concept of the environment is as follows: it is the system of the forms of word-change of one and the same word; for instance *stol, stola, stolu, stolami, stolakh*[1], etc. belong to one environment, whereas *stol, stolik*[2], *stolovyi*[3], *stolovat'sya*[4] belong to mutually different environments. It is clear, finally, that this problem in Linguistics has not been unambiguously resolved.[29] Although the constructions within the model in no way depend on the choice of the interpretation of the concept of the environment, we shall have in view the structural principle of the regularity of the systems of word-forms, and, in those cases to which this principle extends, we distinguish two interpretations.

Interpretation 1. Within one environment we find those and only those forms which are united by a common lexical morpheme and which belong to one paradigm of Declension or one paradigm of Conjugation.

[1] *Part of the paradigm of stol* 'table'. [2] little table
[3] table- (*adj.*) [4] to board

However, we shall only have this interpretation in view in those paragraphs where an analogue of the "part of speech" is being constructed. But the concept of the part of speech has, it seems, real value only where words appear in their "primary" function,[30] i.e. where nouns signify objects, adjectives signify constant features and verbs variable features, etc. Therefore when, later on, we shall be constructing an analogue of the "part of speech", we shall have in view only words (in the first place, nouns) in their primary function.

It is essential to recognize that our criterion for the belonging to one paradigm of Declension or Conjugation is not very exact. "The concepts of 'declension' and 'conjugation' have themselves never been precisely defined, and have been taken directly from tradition[1]."[31] Starting from this, we shall, except for §27 and §28, have in view for "environment" another concept, namely, the assembly of words which are connected by a common lexical morpheme; and if, for one of them having the form

$$A + B$$

stem   suffix + ending,

there has been found a word of the form

$$A' + B,$$

then, for the majority of others having the form

$$A + B',$$

there will be found a word of the form

$$A' + B'.$$

In other words we shall have in view words which can be united among themselves by the principle of identity of stems by the so-called method of squares (cf. §31). In this way we obtain the following interpretation of the concept "environment".

Interpretation 2. Within one environment there occur forms having a common stem and formed by the most productive flexions and suffixes, almost without limitations as to their usage.

In this way participles, infinitives, gerunds, "nomina agentis" and "nomina actionis" fall into the environment of a particular verb-form.

In some Slavonic Languages, for instance in Czech and Slovak, it follows by the second Interpretation that it is necessary to place possessive adjectives in the environment of the noun signifying an

[1] [Translation – *N.F.C.O.* and *A.S.C.R.*]

animate being. N. S. Trubetzkoy's opinion regarding similar adjectives in Old Slavonic is very interesting:

"From every noun signifying an animate being, there is formed a possessive adjective which belongs to the paradigm of declension of this noun, just as participles belong to the paradigm of conjugation of the verb[1]."[32]

This interpretation will be kept in view in the greater part of the present work. Bearing in mind, however, that each of our interpretations is bound up with considerable difficulties, we take yet another interpretation.

Interpretation 3. All words with a common lexical morpheme (lexeme) without any limitations as to the productivity of the endings and suffixes fall within one environment.

In §30 and §47 we show how the criteria for the transition from Interpretation 3 to Interpretation 2 can be formulated within the model itself.

It is essential to make one further observation regarding the concept of the environment. At the beginning of this paragraph it was stated that the division into environments can be taken as a division into non-intersecting classes. But, if we bear Interpretations 1 and 2 in mind, the systems of forms of two different words can intersect:

I	II
pech'[2]	*pech'*[3]
peku	*pechi*
pechesh'	*pech'yu*
pek	. . .
pekli	*pechei*
. . .	. . .

We have already indicated that it is possible to start from Interpretation 3, in which we shall have only the one environment connected by the common morpheme *pek/pech'*.

But Interpretations 1 and 2 are most important from the point of view of the linguistic interpretations of the formal constructions of a series of our paragraphs. It is also possible to consider that grammatical homonyms of the type *pech'* have been given to us in advance as two words (*pech'*₁ and *pech'*₂), and that all homonyms have been equipped with similar indices. We show later on that there also exist formal models for differentiating homonyms.

---

[1] [Translation – *N.F.C.O. and A.S.C.R.*]
[2] to cook (*and part of its paradigm*).   [3] stove (*and part of its paradigm*).

§25 · *The grammatical categories*

The last concept which will be considered in what follows as given from without, that is, as not definable in the terms of the model, is the concept of the grammatical category (sometimes we shall simply say "category"). In other words, we shall consider that we are given certain abstract concepts which may be called grammatical categories,[33] and, for each word, the categories it is coordinated with are indicated. Generally speaking, one word may here be coordinated with several categories. The mapping of the set of words onto the set of categories leads to a certain division of words into classes which intersect among themselves. It is convenient to call these classes categories too. In what follows we shall use the term *category* in this second sense.

This sort of idea of the category is close to that suggested by A. M. Peshkovskii. In fact, for Peshkovskii, the grammatical (or, as he put it, the formal) category is a set of words characterized by a common grammatical meaning and a common formal mark (at least as far as a part of the words goes).[34] For example, following Peshkovskii, it is possible to distinguish the following formal categories of words:

Nom. case	Dat. case	Acc. case	Singular	Plural
korova[1]	*korove*	*korovu*	*korova*	*korovy*
korovy	*korovam*	*korov*	*korove*	*korov*
lampa[2]	*lampe*	*lampu*	*korovu*	*lampy*
lampy	*lampam*	*lampy*	*lampa*	etc.
stol[3]	etc.	etc.	*lampe*	
stoly			*lampu*	
chelovek[4]			*stol*	
lyudi[5]			*stolu*	
okno[6]			*chelovek*	
okna			etc.	
telo[7]				
tela				
pal'to[8]				
etc.				

[1] cow   [2] lamp   [3] table   [4] man
[5] people   [6] window   [7] body   [8] coat

Fem. gender	Masc. gender	Neut. gender	Animate	In-animate
korova	*stol*	*okno*	*korova*	*stol*
korovy	*stolu*	*telo*	*lan'*[1]	*okno*
korov	*chelovek*	*oknu*	*korovu*	*stolu*
korovam	*cheloveku*	*telu*	*lani*	*oknu*
lampa	etc.	*pal'to*	*chelovek*	*pal'to*
lampy		etc.	*lyudi*	etc.
etc.			etc.	

Since we see that the word corresponds to a whole series of categories simultaneously, it is useful to introduce a concept corresponding to the assembly – or more precisely to the conjunction – of several categories.

We shall say that two words x and y belong to one *elementary grammatical category*,[35] if the categories to which x and y simultaneously belong coincide; in other words, if x belongs to all the categories to which y belongs, and y belongs to all the categories to which x belongs.

In our example, *oknu* and *telu* belong to one elementary category (the conjunction of categories: dative case and singular number, neuter gender and inanimateness),[36] but *chelovek* and *stol* to different ones, because *stol* belongs to the category "inanimate" and *chelovek* to the category "animate". Cases of the disjunctive connection of elementary categories (for instance, *stol* corresponds to the disjunction of the two conjunctions: masculine gender and singular number, and inanimateness and nominative case, or masculine gender and singular number, inanimateness and accusative case) will be discussed in §32.

In what follows, we shall need a classification of categories according to the relation of these categories to the environments. Here it is useful to distinguish two types of category:

1. Some categories are constructed in such a way that, if a word x from environment $\Gamma(x)$ belongs to this category, then any word from $\Gamma(x)$ belongs to this category. We call these categories *paradigmatic*. Examples of the paradigmatic categories of the noun are: the masculine gender, the feminine gender, the neuter gender, and animateness.

[1] doe

2. We call any category which does not possess this property *non-paradigmatic*. Examples of the non-paradigmatic categories of the noun are: the plural number, the dative case etc. (The difference between the paradigmatic and non-paradigmatic categories coincides to a considerable extent with the difference between Peshkovskii's non-syntactic and syntactic categories; in the following paragraph we see that there exists yet another possibility of getting closer to these categories of Peshkovskii.)

At the start of the paragraph we observed that the grammatical category is an initial concept, given from without. In other words, it does not depend on other initial concepts. For a reasonable linguistic interpretation of our models it is useful, however, for the establishment of the categories to be connected in a definite way with the establishment of the environments.

For the present, we can only make this requirement with respect to the non-paradigmatic categories. We shall discuss the data for the number of paradigmatic categories in §29. The requirement necessary for the number of non-paradigmatic categories is as follows.

If two words x and y, belonging to one environment, belong to different families, then there must exist a pair of non-paradigmatic categories K_1 and K_2 such that x belongs to K_1 and does not belong to K_2, and y belongs to K_2 and does not belong to K_1.

Now we have finished the construction of the initial concepts, in terms of which all the succeeding models are built.

§26 · *On the so-called isomorphism between Phonology and Grammar*

Isomorphism[37] between the phonological and the morphological system is often discussed. It will be shown below how it is possible to reflect this problem in our terms.

We have agreed that we are given a set of grammatical categories, such as the feminine gender, the plural number, animateness, etc.; furthermore, every word is coordinated with a subset of the whole set of categories, namely with an elementary grammatical category.

We shall call two categories *consistent* in a given language if there exists at least one word coordinated with an elementary category which belongs simultaneously to both categories.

In the opposite case, we shall speak of inconsistent categories. Examples of pairs of mutually consistent categories are: the feminine gender, the plural number, inanimateness.

We shall call two categories K_1 and K_2 *homogeneous* if they are inconsistent, and if there exists at least one word of the given language such that the substitution of K_1 for K_2 (or K_2 for K_1) in the subset of categories corresponding to it leads to the assembly of categories corresponding to a certain word of the given language.

Examples of homogeneous categories in Russian are: the masculine gender, the feminine gender and the neuter gender. Non-homogeneous inconsistent categories are the past tense and the dative case.

In this paragraph we shall operate, not with words, but with the assemblies corresponding to them, or with n-fold categories.

In this way, to every registered phrase there corresponds a succession consisting of n-fold categories.

We shall call the category K_1 *bound* with respect to the category K_2 in a given position if the occurrence of K_1 is conditioned by the presence of K_2 in one of the preceding or following n's in the succession corresponding to the given phrase.

If the category K_1 is bound with respect to K_2 in every position, it is called *non-morphological*. The remaining categories are called *morphological* (cf. p. 165 footnote 33). The feminine gender, or the dative case of adjectives, is an example of a non-morphological category.

If a morphological category is bound in a given position, then we shall call the given position the *position of neutralization*[38] of the contrast of the given category and all those homogeneous with it. For example, the position after *chtoby* in Russian phrases of type "Ya khochu, *chtoby* on *prishel*"[1], is a position of neutralization of the category "past tense" with respect to the category homogeneous with it, "non-past tense".

Note. Our definition of neutralization is narrower and, it seems, more formal than that suggested by the Czech philologist, B. Trnka. Thus, the English example quoted by him, *My brothers are merchants*, is, from our point of view, neutralization in the position of the predicate, since, here, the category of the plural number for the word *merchants* is bound with respect to the category of the plural number in the word *brothers*. Trnka also considers this a case of neutralization, but for different reasons: "the plural form *merchants* does not denote two, or more, individuals, as is the case with the governing substantive

[1] I / wish / that / he / would come.

brothers, but a merchant without any numerical qualification".[39] In connection with this, certain examples of neutralization quoted by Trnka (for instance, the elimination of the contrast between the singular and plural number in all positions except the subject of the sentence in certain Dravidian Languages) do not fit in with our definition of neutralization.

We now call any assembly which consists of n morphological categories coordinated with a certain word a "grammateme".

We call the assembly of $n-1$ categories coinciding for two grammatemes an "archigrammateme".

The reader will already have observed that it is possible to establish a one-one correspondence preserving all the relations between the terms of this paragraph and the phonological terms of Chapter II (for instance, the term "grammateme" is related to the term "morphological category" as the term "phoneme" is to the term "relevant mark").

Suppose now that the grammatemes of a certain subsystem are arranged in the same way as the phonemes were arranged (the procedure from §12 can be completely rewritten with the substitution of the word "grammateme" for "phoneme"). We obtain an ordered system of grammatemes possessing the very same abstract properties as the system of §12.

In particular, we define a concept of "categorical homogeneity" analogous to the concept of phonological homogeneity; we define the concept of the empty cell just as in §13 (replacing the words "mark" and "phoneme" by the words "category" and "grammateme"). Obviously, then, statements analogous to Theorems 2.1-2.5 can be made. For instance:

Theorem 3.1. If a grammatical subsystem has no empty cells, then it is categorically homogeneous.

In this way, we see that it is really very easy to construct an isomorphism between the terminological systems. As far as the actual objects are concerned, the position is here somewhat more complicated. The basic difficulty here is, it seems, the following. In Phonology, it is relatively easy to verify all the positions of a sound in order to establish whether or not a certain mark is bound. It is, in practice, impossible to verify all positions for words in order to establish whether or not a category is morphological (in the sense of the given definition). Consider the *cases* as an example. It would seem that all the cases of the noun, for instance, in Russian, with the exception of the nominative, are bound by position (let us say, by being governed). However, it is possible to find positions where, for instance, the accusative case can be replaced by the genitive ("dai mne *vino*"[1] – "dai mne *vina*"), the instrumental by the nominative ("on byl *poet*"[2] – "on byl *poetom*", "*techenie* otneslo lodku"[3] – "*techeniem* otneslo lodku"), the genitive by the instrumental "(polnyi *myslei*"[4] – "polnyi *myslyami*"), the instrumental by the accusative ("on shvyryal v nee *kamnyami*"[5] – "on shvyryal v nee *kamni*"). It is possible to quote an example from Czech of a parallel usage of the accusative and dative ("učiti se *necemu*"[6] – "učiti se *neco*").

A parallel use of these cases (for the personal pronouns) has been attested in Bulgarian too ("Bog da *gi* prosti"[7], cf. "Az *i* proshchavam"[8]; similarly for the verbs *lyubuvam se*[9], *radvam se*[10], *chudya se*[11], *vervam*[12], *sьrdya se*[13], *zavizhdam*[14]).⁴⁰ We must also not forget the free use of cases, cf. the numerous examples of the more or less free use of the Russian cases quoted in R. Jakobson's well-known work.⁴¹

We shall therefore abandon the construction of a full isomorphism between the system of phonetic marks and the system of categories. We shall consider all categories morphological (we are thus coming close to the definition of the morphological category in I. A. Melchuk's work already mentioned).

Now, the grammateme corresponds to the elementary category. In the interpretation of the corresponding models, we shall, on the whole, be dealing with categories of nouns. The fact is that, for the noun, the corresponding subsystem can be reduced to categorical homogeneity, although, sometimes, with some strained interpretations (see §34). In fact, the replacement of one case by another, or of one number by another, and so on, leads, in the great majority of cases, to a grammateme existing in the given language.

For the subsystem of the verb, empty cells are, perhaps not the exception, but the rule. The replacement of the category "indicative mood" by "imperative" or "conditional" leads, as a rule, to the loss of the categories of tense, and so on.

It may be that this is connected with the fact that the categories

[1] Give / me / wine
[2] He / was / [a] poet
[3] [The] current / carried away / [the] boat
[4] full of / thoughts
[5] He / threw / at / her / stones
[6] // to learn // something
[7] God / may / them / forgive!

[8] I / also / forgive
[9] [I] woo
[10] [I] am glad
[11] [I] am astonished
[12] [I] believe
[13] [I] get angry
[14] [I] envy

of the noun as a rule perform only one function of Language, namely the nominative function (here and henceforth we are setting aside forms of the type of the vocative case which are found in a series of Slavonic Languages), whereas in the categories of the verb the most varied functions intersect, most of all the communicative ones (cf. for one, R. Jakobson's analysis of the complexly intersecting functions in terms of Theory of Information).[42] Nevertheless, one may hope that the series of concepts of the models which may be interpreted in the system of the noun may prove useful for interpretation in the system of the verb also.

In this paragraph, we have shown how it is possible to make use of a model transferred from Phonology for making models of the plane of content in Grammar. However, we cannot take isomorphism of the plane of expression and of the plane of content in Grammar as an initial hypothesis.

In order to investigate the paradigmatic relations in the plane of expression, i.e. the relations between classes of words which may be determined on the basis of the analysis of distribution (families) and of the semantic information transmitted by the words (the establishment of the environments), we shall, from the start, make use of models in which the categories, that is, the units of the plane of content in the domain of Grammar, are, in general, not considered.

If the concept of categorical homogeneity has played the basic rôle in the model constructed for the analysis of the units of the plane of content, then, in the models which we consider in the following chapter, the main instrument of the investigation will be the concept of formal homogeneity. For that very reason, a model will be constructed which takes into consideration the correspondences between the plane of expression and the plane of content, that is a model in which the mapping of the set of words on the set of categories is constructed.

Notes 1) In our model, the categories are given from without. It seems that, henceforth, it will be useful to make models in which the investigation of the formal properties of the categories which is being carried out in our work is combined with an analysis of the general meanings of the categories and with the determination of their "differential marks".

We have seen that the establishment of the grammatical categories is completely analogous to the establishment of the phonetic marks. In §10, we discussed the system of differential marks suggested by R. Jakobson for Phonology, which reduces all the variety of marks to a certain small number of differential elements. In fact, a similar idea has been realized by R. Jakobson[43] for the cases.

Unfortunately, none of these investigations have yet reached the stage where it would be possible to apply them to a formal model at the present time. Basing ourselves on this consideration – and also on the wish to facilitate the exposition of material which is difficult enough without this – we operate here with the traditional categories. It seems that it will be possible to transfer all the results obtained by such an interpretation to the case of the establishment of – not the categories – but the differential marks.

2) The idea of differential marks is applicable, it seems, to semantics as well. Some interesting ideas were expressed in this connection by Vyach. Vs. Ivanov.[44] They amount to the following. There is given a division of the whole set of words into "semantic fields", for instance, a field of words, designating an agent, a field of words designating the intellectual capabilities of people, and so on. "The meaning of every lexical unit can be regarded as a set consisting of an enumerable number of 'semes' (or 'semantic differential marks'). The selection of the 'semes' of which the meaning of a given lexical unit consists is determined by the number of semantic fields into which this unit enters."[1]

In connection with this, the series of definitions from Chapter II can, it seems, be transferred, not only to the grammatical categories, but also the "semantic fields". However, the corresponding ideas are as yet only projected.

[1] [Translation – *N.F.C.O. and A.S.C.R.*]

IV Paradigmatic models in Grammar

§27 · *The modelling of the concept "part of speech"*

The first paradigmatic model we consider was constructed by O. S. Kulagina in connection with the comprehension of some problems arising in machine translation. Since, in grammars, the description of the system of the language is usually conducted in terms of "parts of speech", the model had in view the formalizing of this very imprecise concept.

As indicated in §24, this same concept has only limited value from the formal point of view. However, the model[1] constructed by O. S. Kulagina gave the possibility of posing a series of questions extending far beyond the bounds of this theme. This is, first of all, the linguistic value of the given model.

In Kulagina's model all possible B-divisions of the initial set of words and all possible B-structures (§22) are considered. For a stipulated division B, the B-equivalence of the two sets B_i and B_j is established.

B-equivalence, introduced in §23, as can easily be verified, possesses the properties of reflexiveness, symmetry and transitivity. In a given division B, the whole initial set of words is divided into a series of non-intersecting subsets such that any two equivalent elements B_i and B_k fall into one subset and any two non-equivalent elements B_i and B_j into different subsets. This new division of our set into non-intersecting classes generated by a division B is called the *derivative* of Division B and is denoted by B*.

Thus, B* is a division of the initial set of words by which all elements of Division B which are equivalent among themselves – and only these – fall into one class (B_i*) of this division.

Since B*-division is a particular case of B-divison (as an arbitrary division into non-intersecting classes), it would be possible to consider that, in a similar manner, it is possible to proceed from B* to B**, and so on.

However, the following remarkable theorem, proved by O. S. Kulagina, applies.

Theorem 4.1. The derivative division B** of the derivative division B* coincides with Division B*.

The linguistic meaning of the theorem is, it seems, as follows. If we start from the range of concepts introduced in §§20-21, namely, the word and the registered phrase, then we are, essentially, only given one B-division, the division into individual words (E-division). Starting from this division we obtained the concept of E-equivalence. Hence we obtained, essentially, the derivative of the E-division, namely the division into families (S-division). It would seem that we can now introduce the concept of S-equivalence and obtain a new B-division, and so on. The theorem shows that this is not possible. But division into families is only the simplest of the divisions we deal with in Language, and E-equivalence only the simplest of the equivalences. In order to formalize the other more complicated equivalences, the concepts given in §§20-21 are not enough. It is necessary to introduce at least one more division, given from without, and division into environments, introduced in §24, is such a division. In this way we see that there are also important formal reasons for the introduction of the concept of the environment, which we justified by arguments based on a consideration of the plan of content. We can bring into consideration new B-equivalences and new derivative divisions in a model which makes use of the "environment" as well as the "word" and "registered phrase".

The division into types, or T-division, is defined as a derivative of the division into environments, i.e. of Γ-division: $\Gamma^*(x) = T(x)$, all x.

If we now understand the environment in the sense of Interpretation 1 (§24), we can consider that we have obtained a concept fairly near to the "part of speech".[2] Consider, in fact, such environments as: all the forms of the adjective *bol'shaya, -oi, -ye*[1], etc., and all the forms of the adjective *sil'nyi*[2]. It is clear that these two environments are equivalent one to the other; together, they are united in a type to which belong all the words belonging to the paradigm of declension of the word *sil'nyi* as well as all the words belonging to the paradigm of the word *bol'shoi* and, indeed, of all other adjectives in Russian. So T(*bol'shoi*) is very close to the part of speech "adjective". (Of course, this type does not coincide fully with the part

[1] big   [2] strong

of speech "adjective", as it does not include adjectives which are capable of governing, for instance, *polnyi*[1], *bogatyi*[2], *uverennyi*[3], etc., but we leave such cases aside.) Suppose now that the adjectives are united into one type and suppose them to be the only forms agreeing with nouns (we are also leaving aside participles, pronouns, verbal forms of the past tense, etc.). We show that, now, nouns of different genders fall into one type as well. Let us take the phrases:

Malen'kii mal'chik lezhit na polu[4],
Staraya kukla[5] *lezhit na polu,*
Zolotoe kol'tso[6] *lezhit na polu.*

Consider the Γ-structures of these phrases:

Γ(*malen'kii*) Γ(*mal'chik*) Γ(*lezhit*) Γ(*na*) Γ(*polu*),
Γ(*staraya*) Γ(*kukla*) Γ(*lezhit*) Γ(*na*) Γ(*polu*),
Γ(*zolotoe*) Γ(*kol'tso*) Γ(*lezhit*) Γ(*na*) Γ(*polu*).

It is clear that Γ(*malen'kii*)$\underset{\Gamma}{\sim}\Gamma$(*staraya*)$\underset{\Gamma}{\sim}\Gamma$(*zolotoe*), since, for instance, the words *malen'kaya* and *malen'koe*, etc. belong to Γ(*malen'kii*). Hence it is clear that the registration of the Γ-structure

Γ(*malen'kii*) Γ(*mal'chik*) Γ(*lezhit*) Γ(*na*) Γ(*polu*)

will not be changed if we substitute the environment Γ(*kukla*) or Γ(*kol'tso*) for the environment of Γ(*mal'chik*); moreover this is also true for arbitrary Γ-structures of the type

Γ(A) Γ(*mal'chik*) Γ(B).

In this way, all nouns (in any case, those like *mal'chik*, *kukla*, *okno*[7], etc.) are also united into one type.

It has, however, become clear that the concept of the Type requires a more precise definition from the formal point of view. The point is that, as V. A. Uspenskii has shown, if two words belong to one family, they do not by any means belong to one type. (In the Appendix, an example is quoted from an artificial language in which two words from the same family belong to different types.) In connection with this, new definitions are introduced.

We call a language *correct*[3] if any two words belonging to one

[1] full
[2] rich
[3] confident

[4] [The] little / boy / is lying / on / [the] ground.
[5] [the] old / doll
[6] [the] golden / ring
[7] window

family also belong to one type. We call two elements x and y *Re-quivalent* if there exists a chain of elements $r_1, r_2 \ldots r_n$ such that:

1) for any i the elements r_i and r_{i+1} belong *either* to one and the same environment *or* to one and the same family;

2) $r_1 = x, r_n = y$.

As can easily be verified, the set of initial elements falls into classes of R-equivalent elements, which we shall call *sections*.

As an example of words belonging to one section, we have *stolom*[1] and *stul*[2]. It is in fact possible to construct such a chain between *stolom* and *stul*: *stul* belongs to the same family as *stol*, and *stol* belongs to the same environment as *stolom*.

The following relations, formulated and proved by V. A. Uspenskii, apply:

Theorem 4.2. In correct languages, for any word x, the following is true:

1) $R(x) \subseteq T(x)$, i.e., the section is contained within the type;

2) $T(x) = R^*(x)$, i.e. the division by types coincides with the derivative of the division into sections.

In this way, we see that, with a definite interpretation of the concept "environment", we can obtain an analogue of the concept "part of speech", namely, the derivative of the concept "section" (it is understood that the same limitations apply here as earlier, i.e., words are considered in their "primary" functions).

Yet another concept yielding an approximation to the part of speech was introduced by O. S. Kulagina. The *morphological class* $N(x)$ of the word x will be our name for the set of words x' such that at least one of the following conditions is fulfilled:

1) $\Gamma(x) \cap S(x') \neq 0$,

2) $\Gamma(x') \cap S(x) \neq 0$.

In other words, there are united into one morphological class words such that, in the family of one of them, there is a word from the environment of the other. In languages where the morphological classes form a division (for instance, French), the derivative division of the division into classes is also fairly close to the part of speech (for the connection between these divisions, see Kulagina and also §29).

[1] table (*inst. sg.*)   [2] chair

§28 · Simplicity and homogeneity of Language

A concept of extreme importance for all the later part of this exposition is introduced into O. S. Kulagina's model. She calls a language *simple* if the following two requirements are fulfilled:
1) for any x,

$$\Gamma(x) \cap S(x) = x \text{ is true,}$$

in other words, it is required that two words which belong to one environment should belong to different families;
2) if $x' \in \Gamma(x)$ and $y \in S(x)$, then

$$S(x') \cap \Gamma(y) \neq 0,$$

in other words, if there is a word x_1 belonging to $\Gamma(x)$, and x belongs to $S(y)$, then there must exist a word y_1 belonging to $S(x_1)$ and $\Gamma(y)$. This can be represented schematically in a sketch, in the following way. Let $S(x)$ and $\Gamma(x)$ be denoted by the lines, and $S(x_1)$ and $\Gamma(y)$ by the dotted lines. Then the dotted lines must intersect in some point y_1.

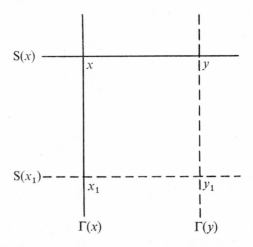

Since each of these requirements has a definite linguistic meaning, we give them special names. We shall call the first requirement the requirement of the *simplicity* of the language, and the second requirement the requirement of the *formal homogeneity* of the language. The second concept plays such an essential rôle in the succeeding discussion and will be used so often that, in contexts where this concept must not be confused with categorical homogeneity, we shall simply speak of the homogeneity of a language, dropping the adjective "formal".

The requirement of simplicity is, it seems, fulfilled in Russian and in other Slavonic languages. Admittedly, in a series of languages, pairs of the type *professora* and *professory*[1] do occur, and this contravenes the requirement of simplicity.

In this connection, it is useful to introduce the following concepts. We shall speak of an *eliminable non-simplicity* in the case that there exist two different grammatical categories K_1 and K_2 such that, of two words x_1 and x_2 belonging to one environment and to one family, x_1 would belong to K_1 but would not belong to K_2, and x_2 would belong to K_2 but would not belong to K_1. In the opposite case we shall speak of *non-eliminable non-simplicity*.

Note. If the establishment of the categories in the model depends only on the properties of the family and of the environments, the concept of eliminable and non-eliminable simplicity within the model does not make sense. However, it is very convenient for the interpretation of the model. So it is evident that, in the example quoted from Russian, we are dealing with eliminable non-simplicity, as in no grammatical system will the words *professory* and *professora* not belong, it seems, to some two different categories.

We encounter a case of what is, in principle, one of non-eliminable non-simplicity in the analysis of Finno-Ugrian languages, for instance, Finnish or Estonian. Thus, in Estonian, the forms of the comitative ("Kaasaütlev") belong to the same family as the forms of the abessive ("Ilmaütlev"); i.e. one can, for instance, substitute for the comitative *rõõmuga* the abessive *rõõmuta*, and vice versa, without contravening the correctness of the grammatical phrase. Cf. "Suure *rõõmuga* tulen sinna" 'I shall come there with great joy'; "Suure *rõõmuta* tulen sinna" 'I shall come there without great joy'. Cases of non-eliminable non-simplicity are interesting in that they form an insuperable obstacle to a strictly distributive analysis, that is, distributive analysis presupposes the simplicity of the language.

From the typological point of view the situation in the case-system of the Finno-Ugrian languages can, to some extent, be compared with the equivalence of various verbal forms in Russian, for instance, *stuchal*[2], *stuknul*[3], and also *stuchit*[4], *stuchal* and, evidently, *stuchal by*[5] (if we consider this as one word-form) belong

---

[1] *Both nom. acc. pl.*   [2] was knocking
[3] knocked   [4] is knocking   [5] would knock

to the paradigm *stuchat'*. For some fragment of Russian these forms appear as equivalent, cf. "Vchera on *stuchit* ko mne"[1] – praesens historicum; "Vchera on *stuchal* ko mne"; "Vchera on *stuchal by* ko mne".

From these examples it is evident that *stuchit* can be replaced by *stuchal* and vice versa. In this connection it is interesting to recall that A. M. Peshkovskii considered the aspectual forms (of type *kol'nul – kolol*[2]) as "non-syntactic" and, at the same time, was inclined to include the forms of tense and mood among the "non-syntactic" things.[4]

Admittedly, in Russian, there is a change of the verb in the past tense according to gender and this prevents us from uniting *stuchal* and *stuchala* in one family (this does not, of course, extend to forms of the aspect). But, for instance, in German, *sagte* and *sagt*, *spräche*, *sprach* and *spricht*, belong to one family and to one paradigm, i.e. German is not simple.

The second requirement, the requirement of homogeneity, is even more important than the first, although, as will be evident later, there apparently do not exist any languages which actually are homogeneous.

It at once became clear that Russian was not a homogeneous language. In fact $\Gamma(stul^{[3]}) \cap S(réki^{[4]}) = stul'ya^{[5]}$ (the word *stul'ya* belongs to the environment of the word *stul* and to the same family as the word *réki*).

$S(stul) \cap \Gamma(réki) = 0$ (there is no word belonging to the environment of the word *réki* which would go into the family containing the word *stul*).

One can represent this in a sketch (opposite).

The environments are enclosed by the continuous lines and the families by dotted ones. The intersection of the family S(*réki*) with the environment $\Gamma(stul'ya)$ is shaded.

Previously, many people (including the author[5]) considered that French was an example of a homogeneous language. The fact is that one of the causes of non-homogeneity, for instance, in Russian, is the "glueing together" of the families in the plural number. In French this glueing together does not happen. But in French there are *pluralia* and *singularia tantum*, that is, words which are used only in the plural or only in the singular number, for instance

[1] Yesterday / he / knocks / to / me (*i.e., at my door*).
[2] pierced   [3] chair   [4] rivers   [5] chairs

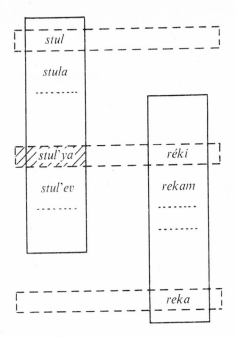

mœurs. Therefore:

$$S(\textit{mœurs}) \cap \Gamma(\textit{vertus}) = \textit{vertus},$$
$$\Gamma(\textit{mœurs}) \cap S(\textit{vertu}) = 0.$$

The concept of homogeneity is above all useful as a model, as a particular abstraction.

In particular, the concept of formal homogeneity is connected in the following way with the concept of correctness introduced earlier.

Theorem 4.3. (due to Uspenskii). Any formally homogeneous language is a correct language.

The concept *approximation to homogeneity* is of still greater importance, although, as yet, no one has succeeded in formalizing this concept. We only show that, in the analysis of actual languages and in the mutual comparison of them, it is possible, it seems, to pose the question of the degree of homogeneity of a language. So it may be considered that Polish is even less homogeneous than Russian. The point is that three genders are distinguished in the singular number in Polish, as in Russian also, and this gives three different families, for instance:

1) *chłopiec, poeta, śnieg*, ('boy', 'poet', 'snow');
2) *córka, żona* ('daughter', 'wife');
3) *dziecko* ('child').

But, in the plural number, in Polish, two genders are distinguished (whereas in Russian all words of the plural number belong to what is grammatically one gender), namely the masculine personal and the non-masculine, including here all words of the masculine gender which denote objects. The differences appear in the form of the words in agreement with the given words; for instance:

$$
dobrzy\ \text{'good'}\ \begin{cases} ch\!łopcy \\ poety \end{cases};\ \text{but}\ dobre\ \begin{cases} dzieci \\ córki \\ żony \\ śniegi, \end{cases}
$$

or

$$
czytali\ \text{'read' [past]}\ \begin{cases} ch\!łopcy; \\ poety \end{cases}\ \text{but}\ czytały\ \begin{cases} dzieci \\ córky \\ żony. \end{cases}
$$

In this way, to three different families in the singular number (to words of the masculine non-personal, the feminine and the neuter gender) there corresponds one family of the plural number. This position is analogous to the position in Russian, where, to three families (of the masculine, neuter and feminine gender) there corresponds one family in the plural. But, in Polish, besides this, to words belonging to two different families in the plural number (i.e. of the masculine personal and the masculine non-personal gender) there corresponds one family in the singular number.

On the other hand, Czech is distinctly more homogeneous than Polish and even than Russian. In Czech, three families are distinguished in the singular number, for instance:

Masculine	*nový žák*	'the new pupil'
	nový sešit	'the new exercise-book'
Feminine	*nová tužka*	'the new pencil'
Neuter	*nové pero*	'the new pen',

and three families in the plural number, which are constructed otherwise than in the singular number:

Masculine animate	*novi žáci*
Masculine inanimate	*nové sešity*
Feminine	*nové tužky*
Neuter	*nová pera.*

In this way, in Czech, words belonging to two families of the singular number belong to one family of the plural number, and words belonging to two families of the plural belong to one family of the singular. Let us compare all three languages – Russian, Polish and Czech – in the corresponding Table:

Language	Number	Masc.		Fem.	Neut.
		animate	inanimate		
		personal	impersonal		
Polish	sg. pl.	▬▬▬▬▬▬▬▬▬▬	▬▬	▬	▬
Czech	sg. pl.	▬▬▬▬▬▬▬▬▬▬	▬▬	▬	▬
Russian	sg. pl.	▬▬▬▬▬▬▬▬▬▬	▬	▬	▬

From the typological point of view, it is interesting that all these languages could be compared, starting from the degree of eliminability of non-homogeneity in each of them.

So, for instance, in Czech, it is easy to attain homogeneity; if we exclude from consideration all the nouns indicating objects (inanimate nouns) of masculine gender (like *sešit* in our example), then, as it is easy to verify, there will be homogeneity in the remaining part of the Czech language. In Polish, where only two genders are distinguished in the plural number and, moreover, these do not coincide with those distinguished in the singular number, or, in Russian, where only one gender is distinguished in the plural number, it is much more difficult to eliminate non-homogeneity.

Of the Slavonic languages, perhaps the nearest to being a homogeneous language is (if we disregard Bulgarian) Serbo-Croat, in which – for the fragment examined by us – each family in the singular number corresponds to just one family in the plural number, and conversely, cf. *mlâd jèlen*[1] – *mlâdi jèleni, mládo dï̈vo*[2] – *mláda drvèta* and *mládu žèna*[3] – *mláde žène*.

We have seen that the degree of eliminability of non-homogeneity can be a useful typological criterion for the comparison of the Slavonic languages. It is also interesting for the comparison of the

[1] [a] young / deer   [2] [a] young / tree   [3] [a] young / wife

Slavonic languages with non-Slavonic ones belonging to the same linguistic area as certain Slavonic languages. In Roumanian, a series of investigators distinguish a group of words of the so-called personal gender, which may be compared with the personal-masculine gender of Polish. As I. K. Kitsimiya has recently shown, from the typological point of view, we are dealing here, in these two languages, with two entirely different phenomena.[6] It is possible to add the following to the arguments put forward by this author: the presence of the so-called personal nouns in Roumanian does not lead to the phenomenon of non-homogeneity which is so characteristic for the personal-masculine gender of Polish.

It is interesting, however, that, in Roumanian, there are phenomena typologically comparable with the non-homogeneity of Polish, Czech or Slovak. But the matter concerns, not the "personal gender", but the so-called neuter or common gender in Roumanian, and precisely, the presence of a family of words which belong to the masculine gender in the singular number and to the feminine gender in the plural number[7]; in this way, the families which can be obtained in the singular number do not coincide with the families in the plural number.

§29 · *The subenvironment and the subfamily · The connection between the subfamily and the elementary category*

We shall say that two words x and y, belonging to one environment, belong to the same subenvironment – we denote the subenvironment of the word x as $\Pi\Gamma(x)$ – if there is a word w belonging to the same family as y in the environment of any word belonging to the same family as x, and there is a word u belonging to the same family as x in the environment of any word belonging to the same family as y. Thus, in Russian, the word *dom*[1] belongs to the same subenvironment as the word *domu*[2], as they, first, belong to one environment, and, secondly, in the environment of any word belonging to the same family as the word *dom* (for instance, consider the environment of the word *stol*[3]), there is a word belonging to the same family as the word *domu* (in our example *stolu*[4] is such a word).

[1] house	[2] *dat. sg.*
[4] *dat. sg.*	[3] table

At the same time the words *dom* and *domov*[1], belonging to one environment, belong to different subenvironments, as there is a word *okon*[2] belonging to the same family as the word *domov*, but there is no word in the environment of the word *okon* which belongs to the same family as the word *dom*.

In a similar fashion, we now introduce the concept of the sub-family. We shall say that two words x and y, belonging to one family, belong to the same subfamily (we denote the subfamily of the word x by $\Pi S(x)$), if, in the family of any word z belonging to the same environment as x, there is a word w, belonging to the same environment as y, and, in the family of any word v belonging to the same environment as y, there is a word z, belonging to the same environment as x. Thus, in Russian, the word *dom* belongs to the same subfamily as *stol*, since, first, they belong to one and the same family, and, secondly, in the family of any word belonging to the same environment as *dom* (for instance, take the family of the word *domu*), there is a word belonging to the same environment as *stol* (in our example *stolu* will again be such a word).

The examples show that the determination of subenvironments is connected with the determination of subfamilies. But one would expect this, since the definitions of the subenvironment and sub-family repeat one another word for word, except that "environment" is replaced throughout by "family", and "family" by "environment".

It is easy to see that, if, for any x, the subenvironment coincides with the environment, or, for any x, the subfamily coincides with the family, the language will be formally homogeneous.

But the concepts of the subenvironment and subfamily have been introduced, not to obtain a new formulation of the concept of the homogeneous language, but for the analysis of non-homogeneous languages.

In §28 we considered a certain fragment of Polish, Czech and Russian. There we stipulated a certain case (the nominative) and saw how the forms of number and gender were distributed in terms of family and environment.

If, however, we now analyse the distribution of subfamilies in this fragment we obtain the following picture:

[1] *gen. pl.*   [2] windows (*gen. pl.*)

Language	Number	Masc.		Fem.	Neut.
		animate	inanimate		
		personal	impersonal		
Polish	sg.	▬▬▬	▬▬▬	▬	▬
	pl.	▬▬▬	▬▬▬	▬	▬
Czech	sg.	▬▬▬	▬▬	▬	▬
	pl.	▬▬▬	▬▬	▬	▬
Russian	sg.	▬▬▬▬▬▬▬▬		▬▬	▬▬
	pl.	▬▬▬▬▬▬▬▬		▬▬	▬▬

The Table reproduced is of interest from the following point of view. Although, in the fragments of Polish, Czech and Russian analysed by us, different families are determined, and they behave differently from the point of view of the eliminability of non-homogeneity, we find in them analogous subfamilies in the singular and in the plural.

We now consider a more extensive fragment of Russian, including changes by Cases as well. Suppose us to be given the following environments:

korova[1]	*lampa*[2]	*stol*[3]	*slon*[4]	*okno*[5]	*telo*[6]
korove	*lampe*	*stola*	*slona*	*okná*	*téla*
korovu	*lampu*	*stolu*	*slonu*	*oknu*	*telu*
korovam	*lampam*	*stolam*	*slonam*	*oknam*	*telam*
korov	*lamp*	*stolov*	*slonov*	*okon*	*tel*
korovy	*lampy*	*stoly*	*slony*	*ókna*	*telá*

Analysing the registered phrases in which these words occur, we obtain the following families, and, within them – making use of the definitions of this paragraph – the following subfamilies (which are distinguished by the dotted frame).

[1] cow   [2] lamp   [3] table   [4] elephant   [5] window   [6] body

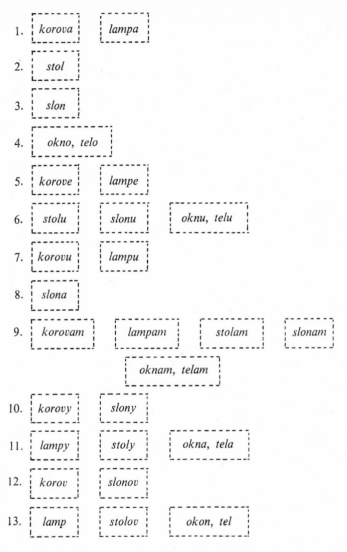

1. korova   lampa

2. stol

3. slon

4. okno, telo

5. korove   lampe

6. stolu   slonu   oknu, telu

7. korovu   lampu

8. slona

9. korovam   lampam   stolam   slonam
oknam, telam

10. korovy   slony

11. lampy   stoly   okna, tela

12. korov   slonov

13. lamp   stolov   okon, tel

Here the following is of interest. The family *stolu, slonu, oknu, telu* divides into three subfamilies in connection with the fact that *stol, slon* and *okno* belong to different families. The family *korova, lampa* divides into two subfamilies, because *korov* belongs to one family and *lamp* to another. Analogous examples can be quoted from Polish, Czech and other Slavonic languages.

We see that the system of definitions accepted by us forces us to separate two words which belong to the same family, such as *stolu* and *slonu*. But this division has actual linguistic sense. For instance, one can say that *stolu* belongs to the category of inanimate nouns and *slonu* to the category of animate nouns. These behave differently in our model, because, in the environment of the word *slonu*, there is the word *slon*, for which there is no equivalent in the environment of the word *stolu* (the words *stol* and *slon* are not equivalent, cf. "ya vizhu *stol*",[1] whereas it is not possible to say "ya vizhu *slon*"). Similar reasoning may be put forward for the words *korova* and *lampa* too.

The significance of the example quoted is as follows. If we remember the concept of the elementary grammatical category (introduced in §25), it is possible to establish that, in our examples, two words *x* and *y*, belonging to one subfamily, correspond to the very same elementary grammatical category or categories. In connection with this, we introduce the following definition connecting the concepts of the subfamily and the elementary grammatical category. Consider a language given as a set of registered phrases with a division of all words into environments and elementary categories. We call the language *regular*, if, in it, any two words *x* and *y*, belonging to one subfamily, belong also to one and the same elementary category (the case that a subset corresponds to a disjunction of elementary categories, i.e. when we are dealing with grammatical homonymy, will be considered in §34).

We now wish to pose a question which is one of the cardinal questions in any grammatical description, namely: how many different grammatical categories is it useful to apply in order that the establishment of the categories should correspond to the formal properties of the language? The initial situation is like this. We are given a regular language for which a division into subfamilies has been obtained. Besides this, there is a set of elementary categories each of which represents an intersection of several non-homogeneous categories. We are also given the mapping of the set of all words on the set of elementary categories. In this mapping, by reason of the regularity of the language, each complete inverse image of a certain elementary category, i.e. the set of words coordinated with the given elementary category, coincides with some subfamily or a disjunction of subfamilies.

[1] I / see / [the] table

Consider now a word *y*. We call the *morphological subclass* of the word *y*, which we denote by M(*y*), the assembly of all words *x*, such that the intersection of the subfamily containing *x* and the environment containing *y* is not empty. For every word we form its morphological subclass. It may be shown that the following statement is true.

Theorem 4.4. (*a*) The morphological subclasses form a division of the whole set of words; (*b*) the derivative of the division into morphological subclasses coincides with the division into types.

Corollary. In the case of a formally homogeneous language these statements are true for the morphological classes.[8]

It would have been possible to introduce in a similar way the concept of the pseudomorphological subclass as the assembly of words such that, in it, for any pair of words *x* and *y*, the intersection of the subenvironment containing *x* and the family containing *y* is not empty. It would have been easy to show that, for such subclasses, one can make a statement analogous to Theorem 4.4*a*. But, it seems, pseudomorphological subclasses do not have linguistic significance, whereas the following important statement applies in relation to the morphological subclasses:

Theorem 4.5. If a language is regular, then two words belonging to one morphological subclass belong to the same paradigmatic category.

Let us now see what morphological subclasses are obtained in the example considered above. The words *oknu* and *telam* belong to one morphological subclass, since there is a word *telu* belonging to the same subfamily as the word *oknu* and to the same environment as the word *telam*. It is easy to convince oneself that almost all words of the neuter gender belong to this morphological subclass. All animate nouns of the masculine gender belong to a second morphological subclass: *slon*, *cheloveku*[1], *muzham*[2], etc. All inanimate nouns of the masculine gender belong to a third morphological subclass: *stol*[3], *stul'ya*[4], etc. All animate nouns of the feminine gender belong to a fourth morphological subclass: *korovam*[5], *zhene*[6], *dama*[7], etc. Finally, all inanimate nouns of the feminine gender belong to a fifth morphological subclass: *lampu*[8], *britvam*[9], etc. Our example shows that, in Russian, not only do two words belonging to one morphological subclass belong to the same para-

[1] man (*dat. sg.*)	[2] husbands (*dat. pl.*)	[3] table
[4] chairs	[5] cows (*dat. pl.*)	[6] woman (*dat. sg.*)
[7] lady	[8] lamp (*acc. sg.*)	[9] razors (*dat. pl.*)

digmatic categories, but also two words belonging to different morphological subclasses differ one from the other by at least one paradigmatic category. In other words, in Russian, it seems that it is possible to establish a one-one correspondence between the number of morphological subclasses and the number of conjunctions of paradigmatic categories which can be coordinated with words of a particular type. We also accept this principle in the model. It is convenient, because the number of morphological subclasses is determined independently of the establishment of the categories (it depends only on the establishment of the environments and sets of registered phrases).

It is understood that the number of morphological subclasses still does not uniquely determine the number of paradigmatic categories, as different non-homogeneous categories may intersect, which leaves the possibility of establishing the categories in a different way, at the same time observing the condition of regularity. For instance, we have obtained five morphological subclasses. We are able to establish the categories in at least two different ways. First of all, one can establish, as is usually done, two groups of categories:

1) masculine gender, feminine gender, neuter gender;
2) inanimateness, animateness.

We observe, however, that such an establishing of the categories with the presence of five (but not six) morphological subclasses leads to categorical non-homogeneity, since, in Russian, the categories of animateness and inanimateness can be coordinated only with words of the masculine and feminine gender (there is an analogous position in other Slavonic languages, as is evident from the examples quoted above). It is therefore possible to proceed otherwise and establish five homogeneous paradigmatic categories: animate-masculine gender, inanimate-masculine gender, animate-feminine gender, inanimate-feminine gender, neuter gender.

We should in fact have preferred this establishment of the categories (since it satisfies the requirement of categorical homogeneity), but formal analysis by means of our model only allows us to estimate indirectly the total number of paradigmatic categories and does not give the possibility of determining the actual establishment of the categories. These last may be obtained only as a result of the analysis of the differential marks of the categories in the plan of content and this leads beyond the scope of the present work (cf. the first Note in §26).

We now turn to the establishment of the non-paradigmatic categories. The empirical fact that, in all the examples considered earlier, two words belonging to one family as a rule belong to the same non-paradigmatic categories is interesting. The cases from Estonian given in §28 constitute the only exceptions. However, since non-simplicity is eliminable in the Slavonic languages, we leave these cases aside, and introduce the following definition. We shall call a language *normal*, if, in it, every family intersecting a non-paradigmatic category belongs wholly to it. For such a language, the number of families will also, within the limits of the given type, determine the number of conjunctions of non-paradigmatic categories (this fully corresponds with the condition advanced in §25). As concerns the separate series of homogeneous categories, here everything that has been said concerning the paradigmatic categories applies.

We now consider how such important requirements as formal homogeneity and normality are connected together. We recall that, in a formally homogeneous language, the subfamily coincides with the family. And so, if a language is formally homogeneous and regular, it is normal, since all words belonging to a given family correspond to a given established intersection of categories, and, consequently, to every category. One more concept may be introduced, allowing us to connect the establishment of the categories with the formal homogeneity of a language. We call a non-paradigmatic category *uniformly distributed*, if, for any morphological class, one of two things is true: the intersection of the given category with any environment within it is empty *or* the intersection of the given category with any environment within it is not empty.

The Cases in Russian are examples of uniformly distributed categories. But Case is not a uniformly distributed category in every language. For instance, in Armenian, the locative case (in -*it*) is only used for nouns indicating inanimate objects (and not even for all the nouns of this category).

Number in Russian is a non-uniformly distributed category, and it is so in any language where there exist the so-called *singularia* and *pluralia tantum*.

The following important statement applies:

Theorem 4.6. If a language is formally homogeneous and regular, then the non-paradigmatic categories are uniformly distributed in it.

This statement is important, because the presence of non-uniformly distributed categories makes any language for which the requirement of regularity is fulfilled formally non-homogeneous. As we have already indicated, it was previously mistakenly held that French was formally homogeneous (cf. §28). But it would be sufficient to show that the categories of number in this language are non-uniformly distributed to have the possibility of constructing an example refuting the suggestion as to the formal homogeneity of French.

§30 · *The problem of the delimitation of individual paradigms*

We know that the environments are, generally speaking, established arbitrarily. Up to now we have started from Interpretation 1 (§24). This solution of the question has made all the discussions essentially simpler, and was therefore necessary for the discussion of an abstract model.

However, as we explained in §24, in the linguistic interpretation of the model, we should wish that the establishment of an environment should answer two requirements:

1) all words belonging to one environment must carry identical semantic information or – since this concept is not sufficiently clear – all words belonging to one environment must have one and the same lexical morpheme;

2) the uniting of words into environments must reflect certain systemic relations in the language or – since this concept is not clear – must be carried out in such a way as to reduce, in some non-trivial way, the degree of non-homogeneity in the language.

Let us clarify these requirements. It is clear that the uniting of words with different lexical morphemes contradicts the linguistic interpretation of the concept "environment" as the system of the forms of a given word. The only thing that can be allowed here is the uniting of so-called suppletive forms, i.e. allomorphs of one and the same lexical morpheme (for instance, *est'*[1] and *byt'*[2] and *khorosho*[3] and *luchshe*[4], etc.). So, words of one environment must determine, with precision down to the allomorph, one and the same lexical morpheme. But this necessary requirement is not sufficient. In fact from the point of view of linguistic interpretation it is in-

[1] is   [2] to be   [3] well   [4] better

convenient to include in one environment any pair of the series of words: *chelovek*[1], *chelovechnyi*[2], *chelovechek*[3], *chelovecheskii*[4], *chelovechestvo*[5], *chelovechina*[6], *chelovechishche*[7], although, in them, with precision down to the allomorph, there is one and the same lexical morpheme, *chelovek*. Of course, intuitively, the difference between these words and the impossibility of uniting them into one paradigm is clear, if for no other reason than the fact that many of them belong to different parts of speech. But we define the "part of speech" on the basis of a definite interpretation of the concept "environment"; that is why we do not find here a formal criterion for uniting into environments.

Problems arise which are not unambiguously resolved by philologists. Should we consider that *videt'*[8] and *uvidet'*[9], that is the two aspectual forms, belong to different paradigms or to one? In traditional terms this problem can be put in the following way: does the formation of the aspectual forms belong to word-formation (two different environments) or to form-formation (one and the same environment)? As is known, this problem is differently resolved by different philologists.[9] It is clear that its solution must be found, not on the basis of external criteria, but by starting from the system of the language, from the relations existing within it.

In our terms, the systemicness of Language, the symmetry which can be observed in it, is reflected as the degree of homogeneity of a language. Hence it is clear that words need to be united into environments in such a way that the language becomes more homogeneous (and, perhaps, more simple).

And so one can imagine the situation thus: at the beginning words are united into environments on the basis of the identity of lexical morphemes (Interpretation 3), then the language obtained in this way is investigated from the point of view of its homogeneity. If the degree of non-homogeneity of the language obtained is high, an attempt is made to reduce the environments in such a way as to raise the degree of homogeneity of the language.

If this is successful, the new division into environments is also regarded as more correct for the language.

However, it may be shown that this question is more complicated than might appear at first sight. The fact is that it is possible to

[1] man [2] humane [3] little man
[4] human [5] humanity [6] hulking great man
[7] *do.* [8] to see [9] to catch sight of

change every language into a homogeneous one in a completely trivial way, that is, by leaving exactly one word in each environment. Such a solution, however, can only satisfy the philologist in the case that we are discussing, if it is a question of an isolating ("amorphous") language of the type of Chinese, where, in actual fact, each environment contains just one word (the following definition of an "amorphous" language can, in passing, be given in our terms: a language is called *amorphous*, if, in it, for any x, $\Gamma(x) = \{x\}$).

Another somewhat less trivial method is the division of the original environments into subenvironments, and the establishment of new environments equal to these. As we know, in this case, the language becomes homogeneous.

If, as in the examples of §28, we limit ourselves to the noun, then, as we saw, the non-homogeneity of a series of Slavonic languages is to a considerable extent explained by the "merging" of the forms of the categories of gender in the plural number. If we now unite the forms of the singular number in one environment and the forms of the plural number in another, then the degree of homogeneity of the language is effectively raised. In passing, we may note that the view that the formation of the plural number is the formation of a new word and not of a form of the same word has more than once been put forward in Linguistics; for instance, Kuznetsov writes[1]: "Following F. F. Fortunatov, I consider the forms of the singular and plural numbers of what is usually considered one word as different words, i.e. as categories which are connected together by word-formation and not by flexional relations".[10] If we stand by this point of view, the degree of homogeneity of Russian and other Slavonic languages is considerably increased, and there will hardly be those fundamental differences between them which were discussed in §28. But, as P. S. Kuznetsov[11] has shown, the logical parallelism of the case-forms of the singular and plural numbers is especially characteristic for the Slavonic languages. And so representing them as forms of one word is quite justified by internal considerations of the system.

It is, it seems, useful to put the question in such a way as to take into consideration, not only the degree of approximation to the homogeneous language, but also the value of the effort required to achieve this. We exactify this side of the question.

[1] [Translation - *N.F.C.O. and A.S.C.R.*]

First, it is important that the ratio of the number of new environments to the number of original environments should not be too great. It is just this intuitive consideration which forces us to disregard the division of each environment of the noun into two (singular number and plural number).

Secondly, it is important to exclude certain words which give rise to non-homogeneity. For instance, the presence of certain words which are *pluralia* and *singularia tantum* in French renders this language non-homogeneous. In principle, two methods are possible for eliminating this non-homogeneity: the division into two environments of forms of the singular number and forms of the plural number considered above and the removal from consideration of words which are *pluralia* and *singularia tantum*. As there are few of the words referred to, the first solution is much more acceptable than the division of all the environments which is produced just because of the presence of these words.

So, our task may be formalized in the following way. We are given a division into families and a division into environments. We need to raise the degree of homogeneity of the language in the most economical way; at the same time we are not permitted to exclude more than a definite part of the total number of environments, and we are not permitted to divide the environments into parts so that the ratio of the number of new environments to the total number of environments in general exceeds a certain number given beforehand.

It is of general interest to see in which cases this task has a solution. None of these problems have as yet been formulated clearly enough to allow a mathematical solution, but the importance of this kind of approach to such problems is clear. Another task, close to the last one, is also interesting. Let us think of a language as a system whose stability is guaranteed by a sufficiently high degree of homogeneity. This system suffers certain perturbations,[12] consisting of:

1) the appearance of new words not having the same forms as other words of the given type (for instance, the appearance of words of the type *pal'to*[1], *kofe*[2], *metro*[3] in Russian);

2) the coincidence of different forms as a result of certain phonetic processes (for instance, in Common Slavonic, the coincidence of the forms of the genitive and dative cases in the singular number in stems in -*i*);

[1] coat   [2] coffee   [3] underground railway

3) the appearance of new forms (for instance, forms in *-u* for words of the type *vosku*[1], *chayu*[2], etc.).

All these perturbations lead to the appearance of certain new environments or change the number of forms in certain environments.

The problem is as follows. If these perturbations are individual ones, it can be assumed that they will not change the degree of homogeneity. If, however, they begin to acquire a mass character, then the system ceases to be in a state of equilibrium. Apparently, one can increase the degree of homogeneity of a language by non-trivial means by redistributing the words by environments (i.e. extending them or, on the other hand, reducing them).

The solution of this problem will allow us to construct a dynamic model based on certain cybernetic considerations and enabling us to show (of course in a simplified, model-building form) how the transition from one state to another takes place in the development of the system of a language.

Thus it is possible to conceive of a definite stage in the development of the ancient Indo-European dialects at which the system of the noun was distinguished by a high degree of homogeneity, for it is possible to take the view that the paradigms of the singular and plural numbers were almost unconnected. The establishment of the parallelism of the singular and plural numbers in a series of cases led to a redistribution of the environments. Non-homogeneity arose, for instance, in connection with the absence of an independent form of the genitive singular case. But by the time of the separate Indo-European languages a new state of stability was being achieved owing to the introduction – in various ways in the different languages – of the missing forms, and thus the filling of the empty cells.

It is clear that such a model can be constructed only if we have a clear picture of the synchronic sections for different periods of the development of a language which have been constructed on the basis of a knowledge of the corresponding facts of generalized formal models (in particular, the type of non-homogeneity must be established, the degree of its eliminability, the character of the subfamilies, etc.). The corresponding data has as yet not been collected, but, nevertheless, it is essential to pose the question of constructing dynamic models.

[1] wax (*gen. sg.*)   [2] tea (*gen. sg.*)

§31 · *Some observations on morphemic analysis*

From now on we shall occasionally make use of the concept of the "morpheme". As was indicated in §17, the formal definition of the morpheme has hitherto been rather difficult. We shall start from a definition based on meaning which is contained in the following words: "This is the most elementary not-further-divisible meaningful unit of language"[1].[13] The weakness of this definition is that it does not tell us by what procedure we can dismember the speech-flow into morphemes.

Thus, for the formal analogue of the morpheme which is going to be constructed, it is necessary to define some procedure for determining morphemes. It is clear that such a formal analogue of the morpheme must be constructed without direct reference to the meaning of words. An indirect reference to meaning is permissible in the class of models which we are investigating by means of establishing environments. We have also seen that the environments may be redefined on the basis of definite intrasystemic requirements.

Now, starting out from the environments and the family, it is fairly easy to obtain a definition of the stem and the flexion (more accurately, of the simplest analogues of these things which it is useful to analyse in a model).

Consider a word x. We shall now no longer think of the word as a primary concept, i.e. as something indivisible, but, rather, we shall think of it as a succession of phonemes, for simplicity, of letters: $l_1, l_2 \ldots l_{n-1}, l_n$.

Let our word x belong to $\Gamma_1 \cap S_1$.

We shall consider a certain section (possibly a zero one) as the *flexion* d_1 and the remaining part as the *stem* f_1, that is, we shall consider the word x as having the form $f_1 d_1$ given the conditions that:

1) for any word x', belonging to $\Gamma(x)$ and having the form $f_1 d_i$, there will be a word y, having the form $f_k d_i$ and belonging to $S(x')$;

2) for any word y', belonging to $S(x)$ and having the form $f_j d_1$, there will be a word x', having the form $f_j d_1$ and belonging to $\Gamma(y')$.

Notes 1) It is easy to see that the definition used for Interpretation 2 of the environment in §24 is repeated here with some insignificant modifications. But here it is assumed that the environment is taken in the most general, the third, Interpretation.

2) In the definition quoted here, the order of succession of the parts f and d with respect to one another may not be fixed, but, rather, it may be considered as a scheme of three different definitions, namely that of a *word-changing prefix* (if d precedes f), of an *infix* (if d is inserted in f) and of an *ending*. For simplicity, we shall only take the last case into consideration, as it is particularly important for the majority of Slavonic languages.

We now observe that, in our definition, it is quite unnecessary that all words belonging to the given environment should determine the same stem, and that all words belonging to the given family should determine the same ending. This corresponds to the actual situation, when, for instance, *chelovek*[2] and *lyudi*[3] are included in one paradigm, and *vremya*[4] and *pole*[5] fall into one family. Such cases are, however, fairly rare. And so we introduce the following definitions too.

We shall call an environment *correct*, if, in all the words of this environment, one and the same stem is determined.

[1] [Translation – *N.F.C.O. and A.S.C.R.*]
[2] man   [3] people   [4] time   [5] field

We shall call a family *correct* if, in all the words of this family, one and the same flexion is determined.

Note. In actual languages correct environments constitute the great majority of all environments, whereas in inflecting languages correct families are not found very often. In the agglutinating languages correct families are the majority, but, here, as we saw in §28, cases of non-simplicity, leading to non-correct families, are met with.

The dismemberment of words into stems and flexions which we have undertaken has been based, not so much on meaning (although it has been taken into consideration indirectly through the concept of the environment), as on a belonging to certain regular series. This method is close to the "method of squares" as it was formulated by Greenberg, and closer still to the method of morphemic analysis suggested by A. M. Peshkovskii.[14] We investigate the word *vodyanistyi*[1] by Peshkovskii's method.

The element *vodyan-* is distinguished because, beside the word *vodyanistyi*, there exist the words:

I. golos*istyi*[2]
plech*istyi*[3]
bolot*istyi*[4]
zolot*istyi*[5]
– and so on.

The element *-yi* is distinguished because there exist the words:

II. *vodyanist*yi
*vodyanist*ogo[6]
*vodyanist*omu[7]

on the one hand, and

III. krasiv*yi*[8]
khodul'n*yi*[9]

on the other hand.

We observe that these series are connected in the sense that, to any element from the one, there corresponds an element from the other.

Finally, it is easy to distinguish the element *-ist-*, standing in the middle. Now we move somewhat away from Peshkovskii's method in the direction of the methods of descriptive analysis.

We have the following division: *vodyan-ist-yi*. Let us now compare the elements *vodyan-* and *vod-*. It is easy to see that *vodyan-* occurs only before the elements:

A. 1) $-oi_1$ 2) *-ist*
   -omu
   -aya, and so on.

On the other hand, *vod-* occurs only before the elements:

B. 1) *-a*   2) *-n-*   3) *-o-*   (the connective
   -u   element in compound
   $-oi_2$ words)
   -ami, and so on.

Since *vod-* does not occur before the elements of Group A, nor *vodyan-* before

[1] watery   [2] vociferous   [3] broad-shouldered   [4] marshy   [5] golden
[6] *gen. sg. masc. neut.*   [7] *dat. sg. masc. neut.*   [8] beautiful   [9] stilted

the elements of Group B, it is said, in Structural Analysis, that *vodyan-* and *vod-* are in a relation of "complementary distribution" one to the other, and are two allomorphs of one and the same morpheme. Thus, by means of Structural Analysis, we have obtained a division *vod-(yan)-ist-yi*, which is close to that obtained by the traditional approach.

Since we have not resorted to the meaning, it may be asked why do we not include in the analysis such words as *vodka*[1] and *vodyanka*[2] (this breaks the state of complementary distribution) on the one hand, and *vodit'*[3], *vodvoryat'*[4], *vodevil'*[5], on the other. But the fact is that these words, as can be easily seen, do not form such well-built and rich series with the words *vodyanistyi* and the others considered by us as the words in Series I and II.

The last example, however, shows that it is necessary to overcome considerable difficulty in the analysis of each case, in spite of the correctness of the basic idea.

We limit ourselves to these remarks, and we do not give a final definition of the morpheme, because the complete formalization of morphemic analysis is connected with the construction of a developed statistical apparatus, and this goes outside the scope of the present work.[15]

In conclusion, we make some points as to the grounds for the possibility of the morphemic dismemberment of the word on the basis of purely statistical considerations without any reference to the concept of environment, which can, it seems, be obtained on the basis of morphemic analysis.

Suppose we have obtained a division into families, for instance:

S_1	S_2	S_3
serpom[6]	*serp*	*sporit'*[15]
sporom[7]	*spor*	*rulit'*[16]
rulem[8]	*rul'*	*pakhat'*[17]
pakharem[9]	*dom*[13]	etc.
romom[10]	*rom*	
veshchestvom[11]	*kom*[14]	
bolotom[12]	etc.	
etc.		

We shall now divide each word into two parts, a right-hand one and a left-hand one:

zero/*serpom*	*serp*/*om*
s/*erpom*	*serpo*/*m*
se/*rpom*	*serpom*/zero
ser/*pom*	

Let us at once pause to consider divisions by which the common element for the different words of the family is determined on the right-hand side in a sufficiently large number, N, of cases.

We call such divisions *morphological*. For instance, the divisions *serp*/*om* and *serpo*/*m* will be morphological for the word *serpom* from S_1. We observe that, for us, both these divisions are equally justified, inasmuch as, with a proper choice of N, both are characteristic for a sufficiently large number of cases.

For the word *serp* the only morphological division will be the division into *serp*/zero, but for the word *rul'* two are possible, *rul'*/zero and *rul'*.[16]

[1] vodka [2] dropsy [3] to lead [4] to settle [5] comic turn
[6] sickle [7] dispute [8] rudder [9] plough [10] rum [11] material
[12] marsh (*6-12 are inst. sg.*) [13] house [14] lump [15] to dispute
[16] to taxi (*aeroplane*) [17] to plough

Consider now in any family (for instance, S_1) that morphological division which passes closest to the centre of the word (for instance, *serp/om*). If, for a selected morphological division for the words of the given family there is a morphological division for some other family (for instance, S_2) such that, for a sufficiently large number of left-hand parts (in our case, for *serp-*, *spor-*, *rul-*, *rom-*), there occurs a left-hand part coinciding with it (in our case, in S_2), and, conversely, for a sufficiently large number of left-hand parts in a second family (for instance, in S_2) there occurs a coinciding left-hand part in the initial family, then we shall say that these families are mutually *bound*. If two words with a common left-hand part belong to two bound families, we shall be able to consider that these words belong to one environment. It is clear that, in this way, we can unite *serpom* and *serp*, *rulem* and *rul'*, *romom* and *rom*, *sporom* and *spor* into one environment. It is also clear that *sporit'* and *spor* will not fall into one environment, as the families S_2 and S_3 are not bound. In fact, we required that there should, in the given division, be a coinciding part from S_3 for a sufficiently large number of words from S_2; for *serp* there are not the words *serpit'* or *serpat'*; this is also true of the words *dom, rom, kom*.

This method, of course, needs to be made more precise, for instance, for the "fugitive vowels" in words of the type *osel*[1] (genitive *osla*), but, on the whole, it fully secures the uniting of words into environments. It can be perfected in another way too, namely, for the case when it is not the right-hand, but the left-hand part of the word that changes (for determining prefixes).

The basic difficulty consists, it seems, in finding a number N sufficiently large to obtain the necessary morphological divisions. But it seems that this way be found by experimental means.

It is, however, important that the concept of the environment can, in principle, be deduced, and it is enough to start with only two initial concepts, the "word" and the "registered phrase".

§32 · *The problem of grammatical homonymy*

Later (§36) an attempt will be made to describe a model of discrimination, that is, the transition from the units of text to the units of the system. For the models considered earlier, where the regularity of the language (i.e. the absence of homonyms) was explicitly or implicitly assumed, the construction of such a model would have been a triviality. Therefore, in the later part of this chapter, the object of our investigation will be the non-regular language. We investigate a model in which homonymy will be determined by the property of equivalence, and, then, we shall discuss questions connected with the construction of models of discrimination.

We turn to the model suggested by R. L. Dobrushin.

Dobrushin's model arose from the consideration of the hypothesis that "family" corresponds to "Case" (see §23).

[1] donkey

It at once became apparent that, generally speaking, this was not so. For instance, it was shown that in Russian three different families are determined:

S_1 – *okno*[1], *solntse*[2], *telo*[3], *tulovishche*[4], *oko*[5] . . .
S_2 – *oknu*[6], *solntsu, telu, tulovishchu, oku* . . .
S_3 – *metro*[7], *pal'to*[8] . . .

For the present we should like words from S_3 to be somehow connected with words from S_1 and with words from S_2.

In this connection, the following system of definitions has been suggested.[17] We shall say that the family S_i *subordinates* the family S_j ($S_i \rightarrow S_j$) if, for any word x belonging to S_i and for any word y belonging to S_j, from the registration of the phrase $A_1 x A_2$, there follows the registration of the phrase $A_1 y A_2$ (where A_1 and A_2 are arbitrary groups of words). The family S_k is called a *commencing* family if there is no family S_e such that $S_e \rightarrow S_k$ and $S_e \neq S_k$.

With every family there is compared the assembly of all the words which belong to it and to all the families which are subordinated to it. We call this assembly an *elementary grammatical series*. (We may note that R. L. Dobrushin calls this an "elementary grammatical category". But we have already used the term "category", and in a meaning which is more accepted in Linguistics – see §§25-26.) We represent the subordination with the aid of the following scheme:

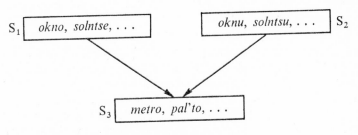

We have obtained the two elementary series:
1) *okno, solntse, metro, pal'to* . . .
2) *oknu, solntsu, metro, pal'to* . . .
The given concept allows us to decide a series of questions connected with the formal distinction of morphological homonyms.

[1] window   [2] sun   [3] body   [4] trunk (*of the body*)   [5] eye
     [6] *These are dat. sg.*   [7] underground railway   [8] coat

For instance, the word *pech'*[1] belongs both to the category of the noun and to the category of the verb. The system of definitions suggested by R. L. Dobrushin yields the possibility of the formal definition of the fact that *pech'* belongs to two forms of category. In fact, we have the following families:

$$S_4 - gol'^{[2]}, stal'^{[3]}, mraz'^{[4]}, rech'^{[5]}$$
$$S_5 - sterech'^{[6]}, doit'^{[7]}, puskat'^{[8]}$$
$$S_6 - pech', tech'^{[9]} \ldots$$

It is easy to see that, here, we obtain two elementary series:
3) *gol', stal', mraz', pech', tech'* . . .
4) *sterech', doit', puskat', pech', tech'* . . .
It is natural to call a class of words *morphologically homonymous* if it belongs to two (or more) elementary series.

So we have obtained a formal definition of the morphological homonym without recourse to meaning.

This result is exceptionally important just because neither the concept of the environment (and the concept of the subfamily which was obtained by its aid), nor the concept of the category has been made use of here.

In terms of belonging to categories, it is, of course, very easy to define the concept of the homonym. But, in our system, the definition of the homonym as a word corresponding to a disjunction of elementary categories – a definition which is, generally speaking, quite reasonable – would have led us in a logical circle, since the establishment of the categories was investigated by us on the assumption of the regularity of the language, i.e. of the absence of homonyms.

Now, however, since the definition of the homonym has been constructed independently of the establishment of the categories, we can assume that a model which equips homonyms of the type *pal'to*[10] or *pech'* with different indices depending on which different elementary series they belong to, is effective from the start. After this we shall consider the question of extending the model of §29 to the non-regular language (see §34). But first we make one short digression.

[1] to cook; stove	[2] poverty	[3] steel
[4] filth	[5] speech	[6] to guard
[7] to milk	[8] to allow	[9] to flow
[10] coat		

§33 · On the connection between syncretism and neutralization

Hjelmslev in his time put forward a remarkable hypothesis to the effect that the phenomena of neutralization in Phonology (in the "plane of expression") and syncretism in Grammar (in the "plane of content") are two manifestations of one and the same phenomenon.[18]

Recently a series of attempts at the generalization of the concept of neutralization have several times been undertaken. The most interesting in this respect have been the ideas expressed by the Czech philologist, B. Trnka.[19] Beside cases of "syntagmatic neutralization" (as Trnka calls the phenomena which we analysed for Phonology in Chapter II and for Grammar in Chapter III), it is proposed to consider cases of "paradigmatic neutralization", that is, cases when members of two paradigms corresponding to two different elementary categories coincide. For instance, in Russian the words *korovam*[1], *lampam*[2], *stolam*[3], *lyudyam*[4], *oknam*[5], *telam*[6], etc., corresponding to the categories of the masculine, feminine and neuter genders, of animateness and inanimateness, belong to the family considered in §29. Following Trnka, it may be said that the opposition between the corresponding categories is neutralized in the given paradigmatic position.

Trnka suggests delimiting these cases terminologically from the cases where the lack of distinction does not apply to all paradigms. So, for instance, the word *nochi*[7] corresponds to the genitive, or the dative or the prepositional case, to the singular or to the plural number, etc. But, in the paradigm of the word *noga*[8], the corresponding categories are different. Trnka also suggests calling this a case of homonymy as distinct from the paradigmatic neutralization considered above.

Our models show that, here, we really are dealing with two different cases.

The case of homonymy in Trnka's sense corresponds to the case when a family, for instance, that to which the word *nochi* belongs, belongs to two or more elementary series (or indeed to series which represent a particular generalization of this concept – see §34). As we have seen, for the delimitation of homonymy in this case, it is sufficient to construct a very simple model, one not making use of

[1] cows   [2] lamps   [3] tables   [4] people   [5] windows
[6] bodies (*1-6 are dat. pl.*)   [7] night   [8] leg

any initial concepts other than "words" and "registered phrases".

The case of paradigmatic neutralization can be reflected only in a more complicated model, requiring the introduction of the concepts "environment" and "category". Then, as we have seen in §30, the family *korovam, lampam, stolam, oknam*, etc., can be divided into a number of subfamilies, each of which corresponds to one elementary category.

We now see to what extent it is possible to extend to the case of a language with homonymy a model which coordinates the subfamilies with the elementary categories.

§34 · *The correspondence between the grammatical categories and the elementary series*

The principle of connection between the environments and the categories put forward in §25 stipulated that, in the case when (at least in a simple language) two different words belong to one environment, they must belong to different elementary categories.

If, now, there exists at least one such environment containing the words x_1 and x_2, then it is convenient to consider any word y belonging to the same elementary series as x_1 and to the same elementary series as x_2, as belonging (at least for one pair of categories) to two different categories simultaneously.

On the basis of the application of this principle to the category of Case, it is possible to reach the conclusion that, besides the six cases determinable in Russian, it is necessary to determine the following as well:

1) the locative case: *v lesu*[1], *v godu*[2];
2) the quantitative-partitive case: "vypit' *chayu*"[3], "dat' *vody*"[4], etc.

Moreover, this fits in with the opinions of a large number of grammarians (for instance, A. A. Shakhmatov, V. A. Bogoroditskii, A. M. Peshkovskii).

The basic difficulty here is connected with the following circumstance. Our principle for determining new categories is purely logical; it is required that there should exist "at least one word such that . . .". When we transfer to the interpretation of the model,

[1] in / [the] forest   [2] in / [a] year   [3] to drink / some tea
[4] to give / some water

then, it seems, the logical principle must be replaced by a statistical one.[20]

We consider such an example. In Czech, the supine is not distinguished from the infinitive in all verbs – but it is in *spáti*[1]: infinitive *spát* (with long *a*), and supine *spat*. Does this mean that in any other infinitive in Czech, for instance, *číst*[2], we should see a homonym belonging to two categories? Any philologist will answer this question in the negative.

It seems that the refusal to recognize the cases mentioned above is to be explained by statistical, or rather intuitive-statistical, considerations.

There is another side to this question too. In §26 we indicated what significance the condition of categorical homogeneity has in the establishment of the categories. And so we must try to establish new categories which do not lead to an increase of categorical non-homogeneity. In particular, this requirement can be fulfilled if we limit ourselves to a certain sublanguage.

Thus, if, in Russian, we distinguish the locative and quantitative-partitive cases for words of the inanimate-masculine gender, then, for categorical homogeneity, it would be essential that corresponding cases for the other genders of Russian were established too. But in the majority of cases there exist no formal indicators for this.

Therefore, we prefer to take the same view of this as traditional grammar, which distinguishes only six cases in Russian. I am stipulating that for the application of our model we have chosen a sublanguage in which such words as *les*[3] do not occur. Thus the way is left clear for a making of models in which, for each sublanguage, there is constructed its own special case-system (we have in mind the concept introduced by Hjelmslev).[21] With such an approach, it would be a meaningless question to ask, for instance, how many cases there are in Russian generally, since the answer to this kind of question would be considered as possible only for specially chosen sublanguages.

After these preliminary remarks we can formulate a requirement with reference to the establishment of categories analogous to the requirement of regularity (§29). We call those subfamilies which belong to commencing families (§32), *commencing subfamilies*. We shall call a language (with the given system of categories) *almost regular*, if, in it, any two words x and y belonging to one com-

[1] to sleep   [2] to read   [3] forest

mencing subfamily belong also to one and the same elementary category. For such a language, the correspondence between the categories and the classes of words belonging to the commencing subfamilies is established by the method described in §29. After dividing all the words into morphological subclasses, one can put the words which did not belong to the commencing subfamilies into those paradigmatic categories into which the words from the same morphological subclass – which did belong to the commencing subfamilies – were put, and into those non-paradigmatic categories into which the words from the commencing subfamilies were put. Admittedly, it remains unclear whether we shall obtain in this way an establishment of the categories which corresponds to our idea of a definite language.

Thus, it is immediately evident that we shall only determine a new category of Case by this procedure if there is, in an environment Γ, a word x which only belongs to this Case. Or in ordinary linguistic language: it is necessary that there should exist at least one paradigm in which the given case-form would not coincide with any other.

The necessity of this condition is illustrated by the following example:

Let there be four cases in a language and two paradigms of declension (a, b, c, d, e, f are word-forms).

	I	II
Nominative case	a	d
Genitive case	b	f
Dative case	c	e
Accusative case	a	e

In this case we could (under certain conditions of which we shall speak later) obtain an elementary series (a, d).

But we shall never obtain an elementary series (a, e), as there is no family which (given a stipulated gender and number) could be coordinated with the accusative case.[22]

Such cases of homonymy are fairly rare, but, all the same, they are not to be excluded. For instance, in Modern Armenian, the accusative for personal names coincides with the dative, but for inanimate objects with the nominative. In Old English, for stems in -*a* (for instance the type *nama* 'name'), the accusative coincides with the dative in the singular number; for almost all words in the plural number, the accusative coincides with the nominative.

§35 · *An extension of the model of the elementary series*

We introduce a series of new definitions. We call an "S_i-phrase" a registered phrase in which the replacement of just one word by a word from the family S_i leaves the phrase registered. In particular, all phrases containing at least one element from the family S_i are S_i-phrases.

Obviously the following also: if $S_i \to S_j$, then all S_i-phrases are simultaneously S_j-phrases.

We now consider a set of registered phrases such that, in every registered phrase, there is not more than one word from a given elementary series (it is clear that such a restriction is completely justified, for instance, in considering the problem of Case).

We call a language in any one of whose phrases not more than one word from a given elementary series is encountered an *elementary language*.

Theorem 4.7. In an elementary language, from the conditions $S_i \to S_j$ and $S_i \neq S_j$, it follows that at least one S_j-phrase is not an S_i-phrase.

Now let $S_i \to S_j$. We declare all S_i-phrases not registered, that is, we temporarily remove them from the set of registered phrases. As we have seen, in this case, at least one S_j-phrase will remain. It is possible to show that, in the remaining sets of phrases, two words previously belonging to one family will remain in one family.

Furthermore there remain, in principle, two possibilities:

1) S_j will prove to be subordinated to some family S_k. Then we shall say that S_j is *conditionally subordinated* to S_k.

2) S_j is not subordinated to any family at all. This case may be described with the help of the modified system of definitions put forward by Dobrushin further on.[23] Here we are leaving these cases out of consideration.

We call the assembly of words belonging to a particular family and to all those subordinated to it or to all those conditionally subordinated to it, a *grammatical series* (thus the grammatical series is a more generalized concept than the elementary grammatical series).

§36 · *Observations on the construction of a discriminating model*

Let us assume that Language is represented as an assembly of categories and environments, and Speech as a set of registered phrases. Our task is to place each word in correspondence with a particular elementary category. In contradistinction to the methods applying earlier for the analysis of a phrase, we do not revert to the whole set of phrases; we make use of information obtained in the models considered previously. We have seen (§31) that the belonging to a given family or subfamily is decided by the ending, and, moreover, if, for simplicity, we restrict ourselves to correct families, then a certain ending corresponds to the information about the family too.

Thus our task consists of:

1) dismembering each word of the phrase into stem and ending;
2) comparing the ending with a family;
3) comparing the family with an elementary category (the second and third stages can easily be united).

It is assumed, moreover, that we have a table of endings, and a list of families and elementary categories.

The mathematical side of the task arising here has been investigated in detail by S. Ya. Fitialov, using a somewhat different terminology.[24]

In this work – which is very interesting precisely from the point of view of making models – it has been shown that each of these operations can be represented as a certain function.

The most interesting observations are those as to the character of the function which places a certain elementary category in correspondence with an ending (the Φ-function).

As we know, a disjunction of elementary categories corresponds, generally speaking, to a family, and an ending α makes the definition of a series of functions $\Phi_1(\alpha)$, $\Phi_2(\alpha)$, etc. essential. It is natural, therefore, to define a new function $\phi(\alpha)$, having the form:

$$\phi(\alpha) = \Phi_1(\alpha) \cup \Phi_2(\alpha) \cup \ldots \cup \Phi_n(\alpha).$$

Further on in the work, the requirements which need to be laid down for functions of this kind are examined, but this investigation has a purely mathematical character. The following circumstance is all that interests us here. The construction of a discriminating model depends essentially on the extent to which homonymy and paradigmatic neutralization are distributed in the given language. Investigations into this have indeed a linguistic interest of their own and they will be able, it seems, to be used for typological investigations.

This kind of investigation was carried out for Czech by P. Sgall,[25] and he has also proposed quantitative methods for evaluating the phenomenon of homonymy.

We take a look at this work. On reasonable grounds the author distinguishes the degrees of comparison separately (where one morpheme corresponds, not to an elementary grammatical category, as usually happens in inflecting languages, but to a separate category, as usually happens in agglutinating languages). If we disregard these, then, in Czech, there are, in all, 452 theoretically possible elementary categories as different combinations of 14 categories. If there had been a one-one correspondence between the elementary categories and the endings, then there would have been 452 different endings in Czech. In fact, this is far from being the case. Paradigmatic neutralizations exclude 394 cases. There thus remain 58 different morphemes. In practice there are 34 different endings (sound-manifolds of endings), but if we count two coinciding endings corresponding to different elementary categories as different type-forms,[26] the number of these type-forms is 116.

It is proposed to examine the following characteristics of Language:

1) the ratio of the number of type-forms to the number of morphemes, i.e. for Czech $\frac{116}{58} = 2$; this index evaluates the degree of synonymy of the endings;

2) the ratio of the number of type-forms to the number of different endings, i.e. for Czech $\frac{116}{34} = 3 \cdot 41$; this index evaluates the degree of homonymy of the endings.

At present the data for the comparison of the corresponding indices of other languages is not yet available, but it must be hoped that these methodics will prove useful.

V Syntagmatic models in Grammar

§37 · *A model transferred from Phonology*

The simplest way of constructing a syntagmatic model on the syntactic level is by transferring to Syntax the model which we discussed in §15.

Consider all the phrases of a language (the "registered phrases"). We furnish each word with an index dependent on the place which it occupies in a certain stipulated phrase. We shall consider words with different place-indices as different elements. Consider a word $a_{\alpha i}$, where α is the number of the word in the dictionary and i the place-number in a certain phrase. We place together all pairs $a_{\alpha i} a_{\beta i+1}$ which actually occur. We obtain a graph characterizing the particular language. Any assembly of phrases makes it possible to construct a subgraph of this graph. For instance, assume we have the phrases:

$$Chelovek_1 \ cheloveku_2 \ volk_3{}^{[1]},$$
$$Chelovek_1 \ khodit_2 \ pryamo_3{}^{[2]},$$
$$Cheloveka_1 \ ubivaet_2 \ volk_3{}^{[3]}.$$

We obtain the following subgraph:

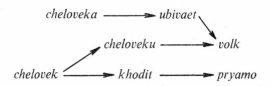

This kind of model allows one to resolve the same questions as

[1] Man / [is] / to man / [a] wolf.
[2] Man / walks / upright.
[3] [The] wolf$_3$ / kills / [the] man$_1$.

the corresponding phonological model (problems of the typological comparison of languages according to certain given characteristics, of the possibility of reconstructing intermediate words, etc.).

But this model is not able to describe the phenomena of Syntax adequately, since, in it, only the relations between words standing side by side are established; cf., for instance:

$$v \to \textit{ochen'} \to \textit{bol'shoi} \to \textit{dom}^{[1]},$$

where the pair (v, *ochen'*) reflects a purely fortuitous connection.

The inadequacy of the model will become still more obvious in the next paragraph, where we consider the model of generation corresponding to it (the language with a finite number of states).

Nevertheless, this model may well be used for the description of a set of phrases where every combination reflects a certain internal connection.

§38 · *The language with a finite number of states*

We shall now construct a synthetic model which is in a reciprocal relation to the model given in §37.

Assume that we have a mechanical device capable of assuming a finite number of states:

$$C_0, C_1 \ldots C_n.$$

The function of this device consists in it passing from the commencing state C_0 to some states C_i; and then the device passes through a succession of states:

$$C_{i_1}, C_{i_2} \ldots C_{i_k}.$$

If the device passes from some state C_j to the state C_k, then this pair of states is called *bound*, and, at this transition, the word a_{jk} occurs. At the transition from a certain state to the commencing one there occurs the end-sign λ (for instance, the full stop). Thus every succession of states through which the device can pass corresponds to a particular sequence of words. If this succession of states is such that the first and last states are C_0, then the sequence of words corresponding to this succession is called a registered phrase and the whole set of registered phrases generated in this way is called a *language with a finite number of states*.

[1] into / [a] / very / big / house

If, in any succession of states, any non-commencing state is passed through twice (i.e. if the device returns to the non-commencing state in generating a certain registered phrase) it is said that the device has a *cycle*. It is easy to see that a device having at least one cycle can generate registered phrases of as great a length as desired. Consequently, a language with a finite number of states can consist of an infinite number of phrases.

It is necessary to note that the states which the device can take up, and all the possible transitions, are given from without. We wish to establish the states and thus connect the transitions from one state to another with the words of the language being investigated so that (*a*) the registered phrases generated by the device coincide with the phrases of this language, and (*b*) the states have a useful linguistic interpretation. We shall now show, from some fragments of Russian, how it would be possible to choose the states and co-ordinate the transitions with words of Russian so as to represent these fragments as a language with a finite number of states.

Thus, for instance, the registered phrases:

Gde kachalis' tikho eli,
Gde shumeli zvonko eli . . .[1]
(Khlebnikov)

may, for instance, be generated by the following device, taking up six states:

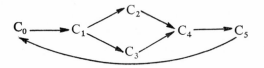

To the bound pair C_0C_1 there corresponds the word *gde*

,,	,,	C_1C_2	,,	,,	,,	*kachalis'*
,,	,,	C_1C_3	,,	,,	,,	*shumeli*
,,	,,	C_2C_4	,,	,,	,,	*tikho*
,,	,,	C_3C_4	,,	,,	,,	*zvonko*
,,	,,	C_4C_5	,,	,,	,,	*eli*

Consider now the beginning of a poem by Bryusov, "Sukhie list'ya":

[1] where / swayed / gently / [the] fir-trees, /
where / rustled / noisily / [the] fir-trees

Sukhie list'ya, sukhie list'ya,
Sukhie list'ya, sukhie list'ya
Pod tusklym vetrom kruzhat, shurshat.
Sukhie list'ya, sukhie list'ya
Pod tusklym vetrom sukhie list'ya . . .[1]

These two phrases – we shall regard the full stop as the end-sign – can be generated by the following device, which takes up only eight states:

To the bound pair C_0C_1 there corresponds a blank

,,	,,	C_1C_2	,,	,,	the word *sukhie*
,,	,,	C_2C_3	,,	,,	,, *list'ya*
,,	,,	C_3C_0	,,	,,	the end-sign
,,	,,	C_3C_4	,,	,,	the word *pod*
,,	,,	C_4C_5	,,	,,	,, *tusklym*
,,	,,	C_5C_6	,,	,,	,, *vetrom*
,,	,,	C_6C_1	,,	,,	an empty word
,,	,,	C_6C_7	,,	,,	the word *kruzhat*
,,	,,	C_7C_8	,,	,,	,, *shurshat*
,,	,,	C_8C_0	,,	,,	the end-sign
,,	,,	C_3C_1	,,	,,	a comma

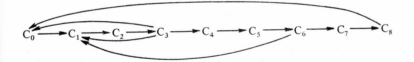

It is easy to see that, besides the above two phrases mentioned, our device will generate an infinite set of other phrases, for instance, phrases of the form

$$\underbrace{\textit{sukhie list'ya, sukhie list'ya} \ldots \qquad \textit{sukhie list'ya}}_{n \text{ times}}$$

Thus we see that a language with a finite number of states can, if cycles are permitted, contain an infinite number of registered phrases.

[1] Dry / leaves, / dry / leaves, /
dry / leaves, / dry / leaves, /
under / [a] dreary / wind / [they] whirl, / [they] rustle. /
Dry / leaves, / dry / leaves, /
under / [a] dreary / wind, / dry / leaves

The scheme of the language with a finite number of states suggested by N. Chomsky and expounded above has one fundamental weakness from our point of view. Namely, we have established that, to every bound pair $(C_i C_j)$, there corresponds one word $a_{ij\alpha}$. However, to one and the same word a_α, there correspond, generally speaking, different bound pairs. This makes the application of the scheme to the analysis of actual languages inconvenient. In fact, the scheme of generation of the two lines of Khlebnikovian poetry was described above. But why should just this particular scheme have been chosen? Indeed, the following scheme is also conceivable:

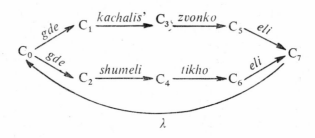

It is of course possible to require that a given set of phrases should be described by means of the establishment of the minimum of the possible number of states. We are, however, imposing a much weaker restriction on the establishment of the states. This restriction says nothing as to the method of generation of phrases of the type of the two schemes described above, but, as we shall see, it has a definite linguistic sense, corresponding to our grammatical intuition. We denote every state that can be established by $C_{\alpha\beta}$, where α is the number of any word in the dictionary which is produced at the transition into this state, and β the number in the dictionary of any word which is produced in the transition out of this state to any other. Now we require that, in the generation of two arbitrary phrases containing one and the same pair of words a_α and a_β standing side by side at the same distance from the beginning (measurable by the number of preceding words), the state $C_{\alpha\beta}$ was passed through.

We call the set of phrases generated by the scheme with the restriction described above a *restricted language* with a finite number of states.

The restriction imposed by us is really a very weak one. We should have wished, for instance, that the combination *khoroshii chelovek*[1] should uniquely define a certain state $C_{khoroshii\ chelovek}$. But, in fact, in Russian, such a combination can stand in any place in the phrase, and we have required uniqueness of generation of a state only for combinations standing at an identical distance from the beginning. We take the stanza:

> *Což Buoh a stvořitel nenie,*
> tot' všecko slove stvořenie,
> *což stvořenie nenie,*
> tot' jest stvořitel!
> (from the Hussite Hymns)

('What is not God and Creator is the creation of someone's word; what is not a creation is the Creator!').

One would have liked to generate the lines picked out by *italic* by the following scheme:

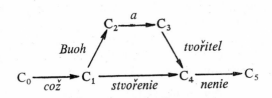

However, with our restriction, this kind of scheme is not obligatory, although, from the linguistic and poetic points of view, there is no particular difference between these lines and those of the Khlebnikovian poem.

The restricted language with a finite number of states permits an interpretation which does not apply to every language with a finite number of states. Consider all the words of a language (beginning with the end-sign λ) and write them out in a line so that no word is repeated in the line. We may repeat this any number of times we like.

Each phrase in this language can be represented in the following way. The word standing in the ith place in the phrase is taken from the ith line. The arrows join words belonging to a certain phrase. For instance, the paths which lead to the obtaining of the phrases $a_3a_2a_3$ and a_3a_3 are shown.

[1] [the] good / man

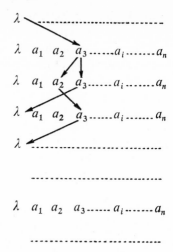

We now show that actual languages, for instance, the Slavonic languages, do not prove to be restricted languages with a finite number of states.

We know that, in the Slavonic languages, word-order is free. Therefore, there exist definite connections between words standing at a distance one from the other. For instance

> Ya, otrok, zazhigayu svechi,
> Ogon' kadil'nyi beregu.
> *Ona* bez mysli i bez rechi
> Na tom *smeetsya* beregu[1]
>   (A. Blok)

Here separated words such as *ona* and *smeetsya, na* and *beregu,* are connected together.

We now try to formulate the property in sufficiently abstract terms.

We call a registered phrase $A = x_1 x_2 \ldots x_n$ a *phrase with frame* (i, j) if there belong to it words x_i and x_j $(j \geq i+2)$ for which there exist words y_i and y_j such that the phrase

$$x_1 \ldots x_{i-1} y_i x_{i+1} \ldots x_{j-1} x_j x_{j+1} \ldots x_n$$

[1] I / [a] youth / light / candles, /
[the] fire / of incense / [I] guard. /
She / without / thought / and / without / speech /
on / that / laughs / bank.

is not registered, whereas the phrase

$$x_1 \ldots x_{i-1} y_i x_{i+1} \ldots x_{j-1} y_j x_{j+1} \ldots x_n$$

remains registered; in other words, if x_i is replaced by y_i, this causes x_j to be replaced by y_j.

Theorem 5.1. A language to which there belongs at least one phrase with frame (i, j) is not a restricted language with a finite number of states.

Hence it follows, among other things, that Russian is not such a language. Admittedly, it could be objected that the above cases of inversion are eliminable, since it is sufficient to describe only phrases not containing an inversion in a formal way. This objection does not seem to us to be justified, as freedom of word-order is an essential typological feature of the Slavonic languages. It is, however, possible to find cases of non-eliminable frame-constructions in Russian (and any other Slavonic language) as well; for instance, *esli . . . , to*[1]; *ne tol'ko . . . , no i*[2], etc. Chomsky has shown that it is possible to construct examples of languages which, in general, are not languages with a finite number of states.

§39 · *Kulagina's configurational model*

The weaknesses of the analytic model considered, which emerged so clearly in the examination of the synthetic model corresponding to it, can basically be explained by the fact that the model investigates only the connections between words standing side by side.

Now we pass on to a consideration of a model suggested by O. S. Kulagina[1] for arbitrary B-structures. But, unlike Kulagina, we shall consider, not arbitrary B-structures, but certain special structures. The fact is that it is very difficult to pass from an analytic model in arbitrary B-structures to the corresponding synthetic model. In actual fact, knowing that a certain B-structure is registered, we still cannot say whether a certain actual phrase reflected on this B-structure is registered. Hence it is obviously useful to construct a syntagmatic model in complete structures (see §22). But, in general, do complete B-structures exist? The following statement answers this question.

Theorem 5.2. (*a*) Any registered S-structure is a complete B-struc-

[1] if . . . / then   [2] not / only . . . / but / also

ture; (*b*) if, in a division B, any B-structure is *either* not registered *or* complete, then, for any element *x*, it is true that B(*x*) is some subset of the family S(*x*).

This theorem shows that it is useful to arrange Syntax precisely in S-structures, for the family is the largest unit in which any structure is complete.

And so, from now on, all the description will be carried out in terms of S-structures (although the majority of the definitions and statements which can be made concerning analytic models is applicable to arbitrary B-structures).

In order to investigate the connections between words not necessarily placed in contact, the concept of the configuration of a definite rank is introduced in Kulagina's model.

The concept of configuration exactifies the concept of the construction and its components, as it is used in Descriptive Linguistics, that is to say, a group of words having the same distribution as one word is called a *construction*, and so is any utterance.[2]

In the analysis of phrases by the method of determining constructions and their components, the concept of "rank" acquires great importance – a concept which, it seems, was already introduced by Jespersen,[3] who, admittedly, only recognized three ranks. The concept of rank has been used in Structural Linguistics, on the one hand by de Groot,[4] and, on the other, by Harris.[5] In this connection de Groot was interested in the relations within a group of words, and Harris in the possibility of extending the replaceability of the word and the group of words by means of the introduction of the corresponding indexization.

All these ideas are reflected in the model to be considered below (although it is difficult to suppose that its creators were directly acquainted with this particular set of ideas from Structural Linguistics).

We now go on to the basic concepts.

Consider an S-structure. We call an *S-configuration of the first rank* ($\tilde{S}_1$) an S-structure which contains not less than two elements and for which there exists an element of the division S (we denote it by S_{α_1}) such that the structures

$$S(A_1)\tilde{S}_{(1)}S(A_2) \text{ and } S(A_1)S_{\alpha_1}S(A_2)$$

are simultaneously registered or not registered for any A_1 and A_2. The element S_{α_1} is called the *resultant* for the given configuration.

Replacing all configurations of the first rank by the resultants, we obtain an S-structure of the first rank (S_1).

In general, an S-structure consisting of not less than two elements for which there is an element S_{α_n} such that the structures of rank $(n-1)$

$$S(A_1)\tilde{S}_{(n)}S(A_2) \text{ and } S(A_1)S_{\alpha_n}S(A_2)$$

are simultaneously registered or not registered for any A_1 and A_2 is called a *configuration of rank n*. A structure not containing a configuration of rank n is called a *structure of rank n*.

The definition of the Configuration is inductive or recursive. Instead of defining separately S-configurations of ranks 2, 3, 25, we at once defined S-configurations of rank n (and S-structures of rank n) by means of S-structures and S-configurations of rank $(n-1)$. These in their turn are defined by means of S-configurations and S-structures of rank $(n-2)$ – and so on. Finally, we come to S-structures and S-configurations of the first rank, which are defined (the basis of the inductive definition).

We investigate from this point of view the S-structure:

$$S(malen'kaya)S(devochka)S(dolgo)S(laskala)S(koshku)^{[1]}.$$

Is it possible to distinguish an S-configuration of the first rank in it?

We shall try to replace $S(malen'kaya)S(devochka)$ by $S(devochka)$. We obtain $S(devochka)S(dolgo)S(laskala)S(koshku)$. This is also a registered S-structure. Is it, however, possible to regard the S-structure $S(malen'kaya)S(devochka)$ as an S-configuration of the first rank? The definition requires that we should verify the possibility of such a replacement in any environments.

We take the environment:

$$S(ves'ma)^{[2]}S(malen'kaya)S(devochka)S(stoyala)^{[3]},$$

where $S(ves'ma)$ is the family including all adverbs of degree of the type $ochen'^{[4]}$, $ves'ma$, etc. $S(stoyala)$ is the family of intransitive verbs of the type $gulyala^{[5]}$, $igrala^{[6]}$, $tantsevala^{[7]}$, etc.

If, in this registered S-structure – it is registered in the phrase

---

[1] [The] little / girl / for long / caressed / [the] cat. [2] very
[3] was standing [4] very [5] was walking
[6] was playing [7] was dancing

Ochen' krasivaya dama stoyala[1] – we replace S(*malen'kaya*)S(*devochka*) by S(*devochka*), we obtain

$$S(ves'ma)S(devochka)S(stoyala).$$

This S-structure is not registered (if phrases of the type *Ochen' dama stoyala* are regarded as unregistered in Russian). Thus S(*malen'kaya*)S(*devochka*) is not a configuration of the first rank. It is easy to verify that S(*ves'ma*)S(*malen'kaya*) is, in fact, a configuration of the first rank. S(*ves'ma*)S(*malen'kaya*) may, in all environments, be replaced by S(*malen'kaya*), and conversely; that is, S(*malen'kaya*) is a resultant of a configuration of the first rank (S_{α_1}). If, however, we are to consider only S-structures of the first rank, i.e. those in which there are no configurations of the first rank, then S(*malen'kaya*)S(*devochka*) can always be replaced by S(*devochka*), and conversely.

Thus S(*malen'kaya*)S(*devochka*) is in fact a configuration of rank 2 with resultant $S_{\alpha_2} = S(devochka)$.

We shall analyse our S-structure further. S(*dolgo*)S(*laskala*) is in fact a configuration of rank 2 with resultant S(*laskala*). Thus the structure of rank 2 obtained from the initial phrase has the form:

$$S(devochka)S(laskala)S(koshku).$$

If we are considering only S-structures of rank 2, then it is always possible to replace S(*laskala*)S(*koshku*) by S(*stoyala*) (that is, a transitive verb with complement by an intransitive verb). Thus the S-structure of rank 3 obtained from the above has the form:

$$S(devochka)S(stoyala).$$

One more observation needs to be made concerning the ranks of S-structures. Owing to the definition given by us, any S-structure of rank n is, at the same time, an S-structure of rank $(n-1)$.

We now introduce yet another supplementary restriction applicable to the determination of configurations. The fact is that one may encounter a case when one and the same element S_k forms a configuration of the first rank with the element S_i standing to the right of it, and a configuration of the same rank with the element S_j standing to the left of it. For unambiguousness, we require that all configurations should be determined in a strict order, usually from left to right.

[1] [A] / very / beautiful / lady / was standing

§40 · The norm of an S-structure · Regular and non-regular configurations

We introduce the following definitions:

The structure obtained from a given S-structure or its simplifications by means of the replacement of configurations by their resultants (by means of abbreviation) is called the *simplification* of the given S-structure.

A simplification not containing any configurations is called a *basic simplification*. An element belonging to the basic simplification of a given S-structure is called a *basic element* of it.

The number of basic elements of a given S-structure is called its *norm*. The plurality of the resultants in the configurations may give the impression that the norm is a number which is variable, depending on which resultants belonged to the intermediate simplifications. Experience shows, however, that in actual languages this is not so and the norm of a given S-structure is a constant number. No one has yet succeeded in actually finding conditions under which this property would obtain.

We shall call a configuration *regular* if:

1) the resultant of the given configuration coincides with the element of the configuration furthest to the right, and does not coincide with any other element of the configuration; *or*

2) the resultant of the given configuration coincides with the element of it furthest to the left, and does not coincide with any other element of the configuration.

Example. Regular configurations in Russian will be, for instance:

1. Adverb of Degree + Adjective
   ochen'[1]   *bol'shoi*[2]   →   *bol'shoi*
   S_1 S_2 S_2

2. Adjective   +   Noun
   bol'shoi   *dom*[3]   →   *dom*
   S_2 S_3 S_3

3. Adjunct   +   Verb
   plotno[4]   *poobedal*[5] →   *poobedal*
   S_4 S_5 S_5

[1] very   [2] big   [3] house   [4] heartily   [5] dined

ML K

It is clear that regular configurations are of the greatest interest from the linguistic point of view. And so it is important to have the possibility of regarding certain non-regular configurations as parts of regular ones.

We introduce the following auxiliary concept. We shall say that a configuration is *prebasic* if it is non-regular and its resultant is an element of a basic simplification. In what follows, we only take account of languages for which there is a method of abbreviating any S-structure in such a way that only the regular configurations and the prebasic configurations are determined. In the further discussion, it is assumed that abbreviation takes place precisely in this way.

§41 · *The constituents and the relations between them · The sentence*

We shall call the *nucleus* that element of a regular configuration which coincides with the resultant, and the *attribute* that part of a regular configuration which remains after the removal of the nucleus. If the attribute lies to the right of the nucleus, we shall call it the *right attribute*; the *left attribute* is similarly defined.

We call the nucleus a *proper* nucleus of a given attribute if it is the only nucleus with which the given attribute can occur.

Our "nucleus" and "attribute" correspond exactly to "nucleus" and "satellite" in the terminology of Pike and Pittman.[6] The term "attribute" has the advantage that it appeals to the philologist's intuition, reminding him of the relations in the noun-group. Its weakness lies in the fact that it has, first, a wider significance, since it applies to the group of the verb also, for instance, according to our terminology, in the configuration $S(khorosho)^{[1]}S(poet)^{[2]}$, $S(khorosho)$ is an attribute. On the other hand, in languages with an isaphetic construction, determination is not an attribute in our sense, as the configuration "determining noun + determined" is not regular.

We do not insist on our terminology; it is only necessary to emphasize that the actual concept of the attribute (or satellite) is extremely fruitful.

In particular, this concept enables us to solve such a problem as

        [1] well   [2] poet

that of delimiting words "of full meaning" and "subsidiary" words (or morphemes) on purely formal grounds without reference to meaning. A word which never has attributes (satellites) may be called *subsidiary*. Any word which is not subsidiary may be called a word *of full meaning*. Subsidiary words can, in their turn, be divided into *facultatives*, i.e. those which may be attributes (for instance, *by*[1] in Russian), and *obligatory* words which cannot be attributes.

Note. When we say that our terms "nucleus" and "attribute" correspond to Pike and Pittman's "nucleus" and "satellite", it should be borne in mind that this is a correspondence between terms used in making models and those of actual linguistic description. Pittman, in the work quoted, adduces ten principles according to which a construction is divided into nucleus and satellite. These can be divided into the following groups:

1) *Logical principles.* Here there belongs, in the first place, the principle we have chosen of the identity of distribution both of the whole construction and of part of it, and, secondly, the so-called principle of independence: A is the nucleus in the construction AB if A occurs without B and B without A does not occur. This second principle is reflected in the definition of the proper nucleus.

2) *Statistical principles.* Here there belongs, in the first place, the principle of the extent of the class. That is to say, if, in any construction AB, one of the elements A belongs to a class numbering more members than the classes to which the other elements belong, then this element A is regarded as the nucleus. For instance, in the construction *budu chitat'*[2], the number of elements which can be substituted for *budu* (here belong, for instance, *stanu*[3], *nachnu*[3], *prodolzhayu*[4]) is significantly less than the number of elements which can be substituted for *chitat'*. Consequently *chitat'* is regarded as the nucleus and *budu* as the satellite. This is, in a way, statistics based on paradigmatic relations. Pittman's other statistical principle is based on syntagmatics. If A from the Construction AB occurs also in constructions of the form AΔ or ΔA, where Δ is different groups of words, and B occurs in constructions of the form BC or CB, there being significantly more of the first than of the second, then A is regarded as the nucleus and B as the satellite. Neither of these principles was taken into consideration in our definition of the nucleus and the attribute. These principles can be easily formalized if a statistical model is to be constructed on the basis of our logical one.

3) *Prosodic principles.* Here belong stress, intonation, etc.

4) *Semantic principles.* These are based on taking account of the meaning. It is clear that the principles of the last two groups cannot be reflected in our model, and hence it follows that not all that Pittman divides into nucleus and satellite can be divided into nucleus and attribute in terms of our model.

In Descriptive Linguistics we encounter the extremely important concept of the *constituent*. We now try to define the corresponding

[1] *conditional particle*
[3] I shall begin.
[2] [I] shall / read.
[4] I continue.

concept in terms of our system. We shall call the *constituent* of a given S-structure:

a) any element of an initial S-structure which belongs to a basic simplification; such a constituent is called a *proper basic constituent*;

b) any prebasic configuration of an initial S-structure; such a constituent is called an *improper basic constituent*;

c) any attribute, the elements of which belonged to an initial S-structure; such a constituent is called an *attributive* one.

In our method of abbreviation, it is possible to proceed in such a way that any element of an initial S-structure belongs to one and only one constituent.

Examples. 1) Consider the phrase *On podnyalsya na vysokii kholm*[1] and the S-structure corresponding to it $S_1S_2S_3S_4S_5$. The abbreviation can be represented by the following scheme:

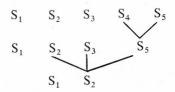

Thus we have the following constituents: two properly basic constituents – $R_1 = S_1$ (*on*), $R_2 = S_2$ (*podnyalsya*), and two attributive constituents – $R_3 = S_4$ (*vysokii*) and $R_4 = S_3S_5$ (*na kholm*).

2) Consider the phrase *Sovetskie shakhmatisty oderzhali krupnuyu pobedu*[2] and the S-structure corresponding to it $S_1S_2S_3S_4S_5$. The abbreviation of it can be represented by the following scheme:

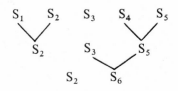

Here S_6 is the family uniting only intransitive verbs of the type

[1] He // climbed // [a] high / hill.
[2] [The] Soviet / chess-players / won / [a] great / victory.

uekhali[1]. (We are starting out from the fact that a phrase of the type "shakhmatisty *oderzhali*" is not registered, whereas the phrase "shakhmatisty *uekhali*" is.)

In this structure it is possible to distinguish the following constituents: $R_1 = S_1$ (*sovetskie*), $R_2 = S_2$ (*shakhmatisty*), $R_3 = S_4$ (*krupnuyu*), $R_4 = S_3S_5$ (*oderzhali pobedu*). S_3S_5 is an example of a prebasic constituent. S_6 is not a constituent, as it did not belong to the initial structure.

We introduce the concept of "direct subordination" between the constituents of a given structure.

If a constituent A is an attribute to the nucleus C, and C belongs as a component part to B, or coincides with B, then we shall say that A is *directly subordinated* to B (B ⇒ A). If two constituents A and B are proper or improper basic constituents, then we shall say that A is directly subordinated to B, and B directly subordinated to A (A ⇄ B). In this case we shall say that A and B constitute a *predicative pair*.

Example. In the first example we have $S_1 ⇄ S_2$, $S_2 ⇄ S_3S_5$, $S_3S_5 ⇒ S_4$. In the second example $S_2 ⇄ S_3S_5$, $S_3S_5 ⇒ S_4$, $S_2 ⇒ S_1$.

We shall say that a constituent A is *subordinate* to a constituent B if there is a chain of components $R_1, R_2 \ldots R_n$ such that $R_1 = A$, $R_n = B$ and $R_{i+1} ⇒ R_i$ ($1 \leq i < n$).

We now introduce the following definition:

An S-structure is called a *sentence* if, for any constituent R_i, there is one and only one constituent R_j such that $R_j ⇒ R_i$ ($i \neq j$).

The following statements are almost obvious.

Theorem 5.3. For any two constituents R_1 and R_2 of a given sentence, one of two things takes place: 1) one of them directly subordinates the other; 2) there is a constituent R_3 which subordinates R_2 and directly subordinates R_1.

Theorem 5.4. In a sentence there is one and only one predicative pair.

Corollary. The sentence has norm 2.

It is interesting that the converse statement is also true.

Theorem 5.5. If a registered S-structure has norm 2, then it is a sentence.

Thus there is another, more convenient definition of the sentence. The sentence is a registered S-structure of norm 2.

[1] went away

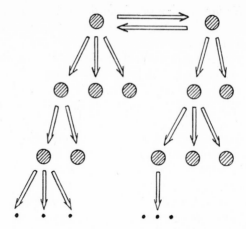

In this definition the concept of subordination is not used at all. However, this concept has definite significance, viz. it allows us to construct, in a formal way, schemes of subordination almost analogous to those which are examined in school grammar. We now know that the general scheme of the sentence has the form shown in the above scheme.

It is easy to verify that school schemes almost always fit into this general scheme; for instance, for the phrase *On podnyalsya na ochen'*[1] *vysokii kholm*

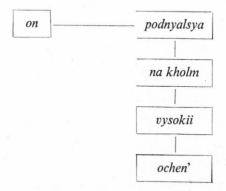

For the phrase *Sovetskie shakhmatisty oderzhali krupnuyu pobedu*, the only difference between our scheme and the school one consists in the approach to the group of the predicate:

[1] very

Our Scheme

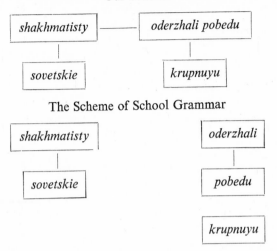

The Scheme of School Grammar

There is, however, an essential difference between our schemes and the schemes of school grammar from the point of view of the elements between which relations are established. We establish relations between constituents, and traditional grammar establishes relations between the members of the sentence, i.e. something that, in our terms, it is possible to define as certain classes of constituents.

But we can define such classes formally in terms of our model, using the analogy with the concept of the structural unit of the phonemes mentioned in §15.

We call a *relateme* a class of constituents each of which, in at least one S-structure, is subordinated to a given stipulated constituent not subordinating it, and, in the scheme, we replace the separate constituents by relatemes. Then we obtain an approximation to the concept of the member of the sentence.

The convenience of the concept of the relateme can be demonstrated by the following example. For the S-structures of the sentences "*Krasivaya* doch' voshla"[1] and "Doch' *rybaka* voshla"[2] two different schemes are needed, if we count the constituents as elements. *Rybaka* and *krasivaya* belong to one relateme at the same time. Therefore, a general scheme on the level of the relateme corresponds to these two schemes of constituents.

[1] [The] beautiful / daughter / came in.
[2] [The] daughter / of [the] fisherman / came in.

Generally speaking, relatemes are intersecting classes of constituents. However, if all the nuclei in the regular configurations are
proper, and there are only two relatemes of the basic constituents,
the division into relatemes is a division into non-intersecting classes.

§42 · *Constructions*

In the preceding paragraphs our model has been based on the
abbreviation of configurations and on the obtaining, in this way,
of certain basic structures (let us call it the first model). Now we
consider a new – the second – model, different from the preceding
one in that, in it, only regular configurations are subject to abbreviation, i.e. abbreviation is the removal of certain attributes. We shall
call a basic simplification obtained by the help of such abbreviation
a *construction* (a construction coincides with a basis in the case that
its elements do not belong to non-regular configurations). An S-
structure is called a *subconstruction* of a given construction if it
reduces the given construction by means of the removal of certain
attributes.

The importance of this, the second model of syntactic description,
lies in the fact that actual Grammar can be modelled best of all by
the help of a model which is a combination of the first and second
models.

In particular, the constructions determined in the second model
correspond to the so-called "logico-grammatical types of the
sentence".[7]

Thus, for Russian, it is possible to determine, for instance, such
constructions as:

I. *Mal'chik*[1] *idet*[2]
   Mal'chik budet[3] *khodit'*[4]
II. *Mal'chik beret*[5] *knigu*[6]
   Mal'chik budet brat'[7] *knigu*
III. *Mal'chik krasivyi*[8]
   Mal'chik kazhetsya[9] *krasivym*
IV. *Mal'chik – poet*[10]
   Mal'chik budet poetom
   Mal'chik khochet[11] *byt'*[12] *poetom*

[1] [the] boy   [2] is walking   [3] will   [4] walk   [5] takes   [6] [the] book
[7] take   [8] handsome   [9] seems   [10] [a] poet   [11] wishes to   [12] be

V. *Mal'chik rozhden*[1] *boginei*[2]
    Mal'chik rozhdaetsya[3] *boginei*

VI. *Kniga prinadlezhit*[4] *mal'chiku*
    Kniga budet prinadlezhat' mal'chiku

VII. *Mal'chik nazyvaet*[5] *knigu "nikoi"*
    Mal'chik budet nazyvat' knigu "nikoi"

§43 · Should the set of registered phrases be finite or infinite?

In §2 we left this question open. Now we must come back to it. The following conception would be very useful, both for theoretical research and also for practical purposes.

The set of registered phrases is finite. It might be, for instance, the aggregate of the phrases of a given book, or of all the books of a given author, or, again, of all the books of the Polish writers of the sixteenth century (as the work of Polish scholars on a frequency-dictionary of the Polish language of the sixteenth century shows, this set is quite easily surveyed). At the same time, of course, it is necessary to regard all the phrases which are not encountered as un-registered, so that there may well prove to be an infinite set of un-registered phrases; but it is possible to leave these out of considera-tion.

It appears that an approach to the set of registered phrases as finite compels us to set aside such an important concept as the "regular configuration". The following statement applies:

Theorem 5.6. If a language is given as a finite set of registered phrases, then it does not contain any regular configuration of the first rank.

Thus, the set of registered phrases in O. S. Kulagina's Theory of Sets conception must be thought of as an infinite one. And so we make use of an abstraction of actual infinity, i.e. we operate at once with the whole infinite set of phrases. As A. A. Markov rightly remarked in his talk at the conference on machine translation, such an approach effectively complicates all our operations. In actual fact, how can we be sure that the elements E_i and E_j are really equivalent? It is obvious that we must sort out all the registered phrases one after another (just the way a machine does) where these

[1] was born   [2] by a goddess   [3] is being born   [4] belongs   [5] calls

elements occur, but we cannot be sure that this process of sorting out phrases will ever stop.

Therefore it is useful to establish in what way the system of initial concepts (given in Chapter III) should be modified for it to be applicable to a finite set of registered phrases, and to observe the consequences for its linguistic interpretation which result from this modification.

1. The first step is as follows. In the definition of B-equivalence it was required that two elements B_i and B_j should be mutually substitutable in any arbitrary structure. We can now relax the requirement, verifying that B_i and B_j belong, not to all the arbitrary structures, but to all structures of a length not exceeding some number k.[9] The definition of B-equivalence then takes on the following form:

B_i is to a limited degree equivalent to B_j if, from the registration of any B-structure of a length not exceeding k and of the form $B(A_1)B_iB(A_2)$, there follows the registration of the B-structure $B(A_1)B_jB(A_2)$, and, from the registration of any B-structure of a length not exceeding k and of the form $B(D_1)B_jB(D_2)$, there follows the registration of the B-structure $B(D_1)B_iB(D_2)$.

The idea of limiting the length of the environments in which the mutual substitutability of elements is verified belongs to Harris, although, for him, it depends on other considerations.

We now observe that our modification of the basic definitions does not touch those models which have been constructed with their help, for it is easy to verify that restricted equivalence possesses the properties of symmetry, reflexiveness and transitivity. And Theorem 5.6, which caused us trouble, does not apply under these conditions.

If, now, the number of words is finite, then the number of phrases of a given length will also be finite, and the analysis of text with the help of the models of this chapter can be regarded as practicable. But this does not mean that it is possible to realize in practice the algorithm of a machine-analysis of text which would still work on the basis of the modified definition. The fact is that, if we keep in view, not the strict concept of equivalence essential for making models, but its linguistic analogue (the mutual substitutability of elements, or of an element and a group of elements), then, it seems, it is in fact possible not to verify whether a given element belongs to all phrases (even supposing them of a given length).

Generally speaking, with such powerful requirements, there may turn out to be not one single pair of equivalent elements in a finite set of phrases.

We have already indicated (§23) that the case of the mutual substitution of two elements for at least one phrase is what is studied in Descriptive Linguistics, and, at the same time, we said that we were not guaranteed from all possible fortuitousness (cf. "on skazal, *chto* bolen"[1] and "on skazal, *direktor* bolen"[2], where *chto* is mutually substitutable with *direktor*). This circumstance forces descriptive linguists to have recourse to a whole system of stipulations (for instance, the need to take intonation into account, etc.). But the element of chance can be excluded if we require that two elements should be mutually substitutable for a sufficiently large number of phrases.

2. We shall say that B_i is equivalent to B_j in practice if there exist N phrases A_1 and A_2 such that, from the registration of $B(A_1)$ $B_iB(A_2)$ there follows the registration of $B(A_1)B_jB(A_2)$, and there exist N phrases C_1 and C_2 such that, from the registration of $B(C_1)B_jB(C_2)$, there follows the registration of $B(C_1)B_iB(C_2)$.

And so we once again strike against the same phenomenon as in §31; in the transition from the model to its interpretation, it becomes necessary to pass from logical criteria to statistical ones.

Coming back from the interpretation to the model itself, we observe that to regard the set of registered phrases as infinite is by no means without value.

With such an approach, we were able to explain all the concepts necessary for the construction of a synthesizing model, reciprocal in relation to configurational analysis.

Thus we examine the synthesizing model corresponding to the configurational one.

§44 · *Generation by the method of development*

Using the method of analysing by immediate constituents Chomsky suggested constructing a more powerful generative process which he called "Phrase-structure Grammar". As we have seen, configurational analysis is a further formalization of the method of immediate constituents, and so, in fact, we shall, as distinct from Chomsky,

[1] He / said / that / [he was] / ill.
[2] He / said / [the] Director / [was] / ill.

conduct the whole discussion in terms of configurational analysis.

Let us recall the second example from §41. There, we started with the whole set of phrases and, by means of analysis, obtained the following scheme of abbreviation:

Sovetskie (S₁) *shakhmatisty* (S₂) *oderzhali* (S₃) *krupnuyu* (S₄) *pobedu* (S₅)

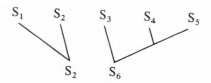

Now let us suppose, on the contrary, that it is known that S_2S_6 is a basic structure which is a sentence, that the configurations S_1S_2, S_4S_5, S_3S_5 are known, and that it is also known that the first is developed from S_2, the second from S_5, and the third from S_6.

Then the whole process of obtaining the given phrase is represented by the scheme (or, as it is sometimes said, the "tree"):

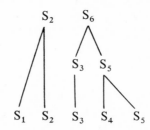

Let each basic structure be denoted by the symbol Z. Then the process of obtaining our phrase can be represented as the succession of operations:

1) $Z \to S_2S_6$
2) $S_2 \to S_1S_2$
3) $S_6 \to S_3S_5$
4) $S_5 \to S_4S_5$
5) $S_1 \to$ *sovetskie*
6) $S_2 \to$ *shakhmatisty*
7) $S_3 \to$ *oderzhali*
8) $S_4 \to$ *krupnuyu*
9) $S_5 \to$ *pobedu*

All these substitutions are operations of the type $x \rightarrow y$, and, in them, one symbol necessarily stands in the left part and several symbols may stand in the right part. Each series of operations of the type $x \rightarrow y$ leads to the transformation of an initial symbol, and this can be denoted in the following way:

$$
\begin{array}{ll}
Z & \\
S_2 S_6 & \text{(by 1)} \\
S_1 S_2 S_6 & \text{(by 2)} \\
S_1 S_2 S_3 S_5 & \text{(by 3)} \\
S_1 S_2 S_3 S_4 S_5 & \text{(by 4)} \\
\textit{sovetskie } S_2 S_3 S_4 S_5 & \text{(by 5)}
\end{array}
$$

. . . .

Sovetskie shakhmatisty oderzhali krupnuyu pobedu (by 9).

We shall call such a series a *derivation*. We shall call the symbols Z and S the *meta-notations*. We shall call the *concluding line* that line of the derivation that does not contain any meta-notations. The assembly of concluding lines which can be established by rules of the given type will be regarded by us as the set of registered phrases generatable by the given grammar.

§45 · *Yngve's hypothesis*

Recently, the great American specialist in the field of Machine Translation, Yngve, put forward the following interesting hypothesis.[8]

We suppose that someone has actually synthesized a phrase in the manner described above. It is clear that he does not produce the complete phrase immediately, but builds the words in a chain one after the other; at the same time, when a phrase begins with certain words, he does not always know how it is going to be completed. The phrase may be of any length (the humorous poem "The house that Jack built" may serve as an example). On the other hand, the capacity of a person's high-speed memory, as Miller's[9] experiments have shown, is extremely limited. Yngve proposes a model which realizes this situation, that is, a device consisting of the following parts:

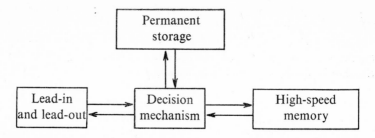

The rules of the form $x_i \rightarrow y_i$ are contained in the permanent storage, the actual operation of substitution is carried out in the decision-mechanism, and the intermediate informing, which needs to be re-called in order to carry out particular operations, is stored in the high-speed memory.

For instance, in order to obtain the succession of words *ochen' sil'naya slonikha udarila l'va*[1] according to the rules

1) *slonikha → sil'naya slonikha*
2) *sil'naya → ochen' sil'naya,* etc.,

the words *sil'naya slonikha,* which may be produced (and erased in the high-speed memory) only when the word *ochen'* has been produced, need to be stored in the high-speed memory until the second rule has been brought into action.

From this example it is clear that the high-speed memory must contain at least two words in order to produce the succession of words we need.

Yngve has suggested an ingenious method of defining the maxi-mum capacity of a memory necessary for the production of a particular sentence in the form of a "tree" of this sentence.

For this, we make use of the following method. At each point where there is a branching of the tree, the branches are numbered from right to left, the branch most to the right receiving the index 0, the next the index 1, and so on; for instance,

For the phrase quoted, we obtain a tree with the following indices:

[1] [The] / very / powerful / she-elephant / struck / [the] lion.

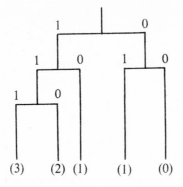

Further, the sum of the indices situated at the branches leading from a particular word to the top of the tree is reckoned. The corresponding sums are stated underneath.

The largest of these sums is called the *depth of the phrase*. The maximum depth of phrase in a given language is called the *depth of the language*.

Yngve shows that the depth of a language is characteristic precisely of the minimal capacity of the high-speed memory essential for the generation of any phrase of the given language by the mechanism described.

One of the most interesting consequences of this fact is the difference between the so-called progressive and regressive[10] constructions in Language.

Yngve calls trees or "sub-trees" (parts of trees) *progressive* constructions if they have the form:

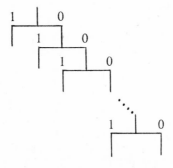

i.e. those in which the branching occurs at points with index zero. Yngve shows that the mechanism described, with a restricted capacity of the high-speed memory, can produce phrases of any length, no matter how great, if the trees of these phrases are progressive constructions.

Yngve calls trees or sub-trees *regressive* constructions if they have the form:

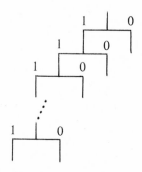

i.e. those where the branching occurs at points with a non-zero index. It is, in fact, because of these constructions that the depth of a phrase increases. After these preparatory remarks we pass on to an exposition of Yngve's basic hypothesis:

1) Phrases which are actually used in colloquial language have a depth not exceeding a definite small number (for instance, 7 ± 2; such, according to Miller, is the capacity of the human high-speed memory).

2) In all languages there are methods of restricting regressive constructions, and, where there are phrases of great depth, synonymous phrases of less depth are used.

3) The factor of depth must play a basic part in change of language.

It is quite simple to verify the first statement. As far as the second and third are concerned, here it is necessary first of all to explain in what ways it is possible to restrict regressive constructions. Of all the methods investigated in this connection by Yngve, we pause to consider the following: restriction of rank, structural rearrangement, preference for binary constructions, especially for the basis and at the points of branching.

Rank restriction of configurations is typical of regressive constructions, namely, for defining groups. Yngve justifiably points out that there are no special semantic reasons for drawing a boundary between nouns and adjectives (in a number of languages, for instance, in Bulgarian or in the Finno-Ugrian languages, some nouns even have degrees of comparison), and between adjectives and adverbs. If, however, all these categories are, as a rule, distinguished, does it follow, asks Yngve, that one should seek the cause in the fact that the occurrence of an adverb, for instance *ochen'* in *"ochen' krasivaya devushka pela"*[1], serves as a signal of the fact that it is impossible further to increase the depth of phrase, which has reached magnitude 3?

Only far-reaching typological investigations will be able to help disprove or confirm this part of the hypothesis.

We may observe that in languages which allow the pre-position of uncoordinated determination, or even require it, there are, it seems, no structural signals for the obtaining of a particular depth, and depth is controlled only by stylistic considerations. Yngve himself quotes the example *His mother's brother's son's daughter's hat* where the depth attained is 5.

But, whereas in English the pre-positive construction with *'s* is used much less frequently than the post-positive determination with *of*, in a series of other languages, for instance in Estonian, Lithuanian, Armenian, etc., the pre-position of uncoordinated determination is the rule. And so it would be interesting to investigate the question whether depth is structurally restricted or not in these groups of languages.

Structural rearrangement, in which depth is reduced through the replacement of a regressive construction by a progressive one, is a fact which can be confirmed by material from a series of languages. For instance, in Russian, groups with the pre-position of the declining comparative degree were once possible, e.g.

"ogromneishii pervogo kamen' skhvatil"[2] ("The Odyssey" in Zhukovskii's translation); "vskrichala ona v *eshche sil'neishem* ispuge"[3] (Dostoevskii, *Unizhennye i oskorblennye*[4]).

Only post-position, which reduces the depth of the phrase, is now possible in such groups.

In the general case, however, it is difficult to affirm that, in the history of a language, any change in the direction of abbreviation of depth has occurred.

[1] [A] / very / beautiful / girl / was singing.
[2] larger than / [the] first / stone / grasped
[3] Cried out / she / in / still / greater / terror.
[4] [The] Offended / and / [the] Innocent

Preference for binary constructions is, perhaps, the most characteristic feature of Language.

Generally speaking, it is not clear why the sentence *Mal'chik lovit koshku*[1] is not usually described in Grammar as the tree:

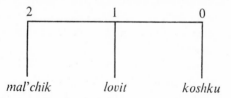

This would be a completely adequate expression of the two-place relation R (*mal'chik, koshka*).

The preference for the tree:

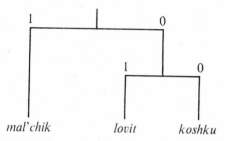

can only be explained from the point of view of Yngve's hypothesis.

Besides, Yngve's hypothesis agrees completely with the assumption that a basic structure must not contain more than two elements (cf. §42).

The general linguistic interest of Yngve's hypothesis lies in the fact that, here, for the first time, a model is being made which takes account of the fact that Language is created, not by an arbitrary mechanism, but by man, and so it must reflect the specific peculiarities of precisely the given cybernetic mechanism.

We see that the model of a configurational synthesis has profound linguistic significance and allows us to pose a series of new questions.

But it has turned out – and the proof of this fact is Chomsky's great service – that this model is insufficient for the description of the most important aspects of Language.

There is a whole series of phenomena which is badly described by

[1] [The] boy / catches / [the] cat.

the given model. First of all the requirement of the replacement of only one symbol does not make it possible to generate very simple phrases; for instance, *Vchera ya byl bolen*[1] cannot be obtained from *ya bolen*[2] in this way.

Secondly, the generation of phrases of the type *Dom stroitsya rabochimi*[3] from phrases of the type *Dom stoit*[4] contradicts our intuitive perception. We should have liked to have had a model in which the phrase *Dom stroitsya rabochimi* was generated from the phrase *Rabochie stroyat dom*[5].

It is clear, however, that, for the creation of a model of generation reflecting all these phenomena, there must exist a corresponding analytic model. And none of these phenomena could be reflected in the preceding analytic models.

§46 · *Transformational analysis*

In the analytic model of configurational analysis we considered only rearrangements which consisted in the replacement of configurations (arbitrary ones in the first model and only regular ones in the second model) by their resultants. We now introduce a new form of re-arrangement which we call a *transformation*. Here we call a trans-formation a rearrangement carried out, not for S-structures, but on actual phrases; however, at the same time, the nature of the relevant S-structure will be taken account of. After these preliminary observations we pass on to the basic definitions. We shall say that two registered phrases, A and B, are in a *transformational relation* one to the other, or *transform* one into the other, if the following two conditions are fulfilled:

1) (*a*) At least one word in A belongs to a non-unitary environ-ment (that is, an environment consisting of more than one word).

(*b*) For any word x in A, belonging to a non-unitary environment, there will be a word y in B which belongs to $\Gamma(x)$, and, conversely, for any word y in B which belongs to a non-unitary environment, there will be a word x in A which belongs to $\Gamma(y)$.

2) For any phrase A_1 with the same S-structure as A, there will

[1] Yesterday / I / was / ill.
[2] I / [am] / ill.
[3] [The] house / is being built / by the workmen.
[4] [The] house / is standing.
[5] [The] workmen / are building / [the] house.

be a phrase B_1 having the same S-structure as B and bound to A_1 by the first condition. A similar requirement is made for any phrase having the same S-structure as B.

Note. Yu. D. Apresian has pointed out to the author that it is useful to introduce a supplementary condition for the transformability of Phrase A into Phrase B. He suggested requiring that, besides Conditions 1 and 2, the following should be fulfilled: for any words x_1 and x_2 such that $S(x_1)$ and $S(x_2)$ are constituents in $S(A)$ and such that the relation $S(x_1) \Rightarrow S(x_2)$ applies in the sense of §41, there must be found in B words y_1 belonging to $\Gamma(x_1)$ and y_2 belonging to $\Gamma(x_2)$ such that $S(y_1) \Rightarrow S(y_2)$ if $S(x_1)$ and $S(x_2)$ are not a predicative pair, and $S(y_1) \Rightarrow S(y_2)$ or $S(y_2) \Rightarrow S(y_1)$ in the opposite case. It may be ascertained that pairs of phrases which we should like to regard as transformable one to the other are not affected by this, but, on the other hand, there are excluded such pairs of phrases as *brat zheny priekhal*[1] and *zhena brata priekhala*[2] or *Pavel sidit v gostyakh u Ivana*[3] and *Ivan sidit v gostyakh u Pavla.*

It is easy to verify that the relation of Transformation divides the whole set of registered phrases into non-intersecting classes, since it possesses the properties of reflexiveness (each phrase is actually in a relation of Transformation with itself), symmetry (if A transforms into B, then B transforms into A) and transitivity (if A transforms into B, and B transforms into C, then A transforms into C).

In each of the classes of phrases obtained we determine the phrase belonging to the shortest construction (in interpretation this will be the construction whose analysis by means of the first model contradicts our intuitive perception least) and we call it the *kernel phrase.*

The selection of kernel phrases constitutes the *syntactic kernel of the language.*

We call the first requirement the requirement of *semantic connection*, since, as we know, words belonging to one environment are, in interpretation, different forms of the same word.[11] Words belonging to a unitary environment are, correctly, subsidiary words (in any case it is true that every subsidiary word has a unitary environment), for example, prepositions. In Transformation it is quite reasonable to allow prepositions to disappear, appear, or one to be replaced by another. Our model must, it seems, be reviewed in application to "amorphous languages", but, for our purposes, this is not essential.

We shall call the second requirement the requirement of *com-*

[1] [The] brother / of [my] wife / has arrived.
[2] [The] wife / of of [my] brother / has arrived.
[3] Paul / is sitting / among / [the] guests / at Ivan's.

pleteness of transformation. It must be said that this requirement reflects an important feature of the rearrangements which are being considered in Linguistics and have recently received the name of "transformations", namely the regularity of a particular rearrangement, its applicability to the whole set of phrases. In the model, of course, such a requirement must be very strict. It is clear that, in the interpretation of the proposed model, we shall strike a series of exceptions in every actual language. For this reason we introduce the following definition. Let us assume that a transformation has been defined for a certain subset of the set of registered phrases, i.e. the rearrangement answering the conditions put forward above. If this rearrangement remains a transformation for the whole set of registered phrases representing an actual language, we shall call this language a *language with full transformation* (abbreviation: LFT). If, however, the transformation can only be defined for a particular subset of registered phrases, that is, only for a part of the phrases of the actual language, we shall call this language a language with non-full transformation.

Consider, for instance, Estonian, for which the following is characteristic:

1) from any verb it is possible to form a verbal noun ("nomen actionis") with the suffix *-mine,* for instance,

kirjutama	'to write'	*kirjutamine*	'writing'
lugema	'to read'	*lugemine*	'reading'
töötama	'to work'	*töötamine*	'work' – and so on;

2) from any verb it is possible to form a "nomen agentis" with the suffix *-ja,* for instance,

kirjutaja	'writer', 'one who writes'
lugeja	'reader'
töötaja	'worker';

3) from any verb (whether transitive or intransitive) it is possible to form a participle – not only that of the active voice in *-nud,* for instance,

kirjutanud	'one who wrote'
lugenud	'one who read'
töötanud	'one who worked' –

but also the participle of the passive voice in -*tud*:

kirjutatud
loetud
töötatud;

4) from any verb there are made two forms of the infinitive, including in this number an inessive form of the second infinitive corresponding to the Russian gerund, for instance,

kirjutades   'writing'
lugedes   'reading' – and so on.

Therefore, if there is phrase:

Õpilane *loeb* raamatut   'The pupil reads the book',

then all the transformations

raamatu *lugemine*   'the reading of the book'
raamatu *lugeja*   'the reader of the book'
raamatut *lugenud* õpilane   'the pupil, having read the book'
    – and so on,

are possible.

It can be shown that, in every language, it is possible to determine a part of the phrases such that it is an LFT. The different capacity of this part in different languages is an important typological criterion. For instance, if we compare the various Slavonic languages from this point of view, we can establish that Polish is, it seems, closer to the ideal LFT than Czech, and Czech is closer than Russian.

In Polish, it is possible to form a nomen actionis with the suffix -*anie*/-*enie* from every verb. If, furthermore, the verb had the index of reflexiveness *się* on it, the corresponding index is still present in the verbal noun, for instance, "Co *się* dzieje podczas *uczenia się* drugiego jezyka i *posługowania się* nim?"[1] The forms of Aspect are also characteristic for the noun, cf. *uczenie – nauczanie*. All this extends the possibility of transformation.

In Czech, the use of the reflexive morpheme is sometimes possible in a transformation (mainly for clarity), e.g.: "*učení se* cizímu jazyku" 'the teaching of oneself a foreign language', but "*učení*

[1] What // happens // during // [the] learning // of [a] second / language / and / [the] availing / oneself / of it?

cizímu jazyku" 'the teaching of another person'. But such instances are, nevertheless, all exceptions. On the other hand, as is known, aspectual differences are consistently retained, cf. *dělení – rozdělení*[1], etc. These examples show that the concept of the LFT – more accurately of the approximation to the ideal LFT – is quite interesting from the point of view of the typology of the Slavonic languages.

This concept may, it seems, prove important for the diachronic study of Language too. One can put forward the hypothesis that the development of every language goes in the direction of the LFT. As we lack the relevant data from the domain of the Slavonic languages, we quote an argument in favour of this hypothesis taken from German. In German, it is possible to form a nomen actionis with the suffix *-ung* from nearly every transitive verb and, in this way, there may be obtained a transformed construction for any kernel phrase containing a transitive verb. A group of the oldest and simplest transitive verbs without prefixes form an exception, for instance, *machen* (there is no *Machung*, but there are *Abmachung, Vermachung*), *tragen* (no *Tragung* but *Abtragung, Austragung*), and so on.

This is connected with the fact that the nouns in *-ung* were only gradually drawn into the sphere of transformational constructions. The number of nomina actionis with the suffix *-ung* has grown gradually,[12] but, even now, this process is not ended.

If the hypothesis of a diachronic tendency in the direction of the LFT is true, then to some extent it is not by chance that it is precisely the Finno-Ugrian languages, in particular Estonian, that are LFT's. The concept of the LFT will, perhaps, turn out to be connected (of course, indirectly and many times removed) with the typological features which are, according to Trubetzkoy,[13] characteristic of the transition from the Indo-European to the Altaic state, that is, with the principle of agglutination which makes possible the widespread, and, above all, the symmetrical, formation of derivative words.

Let us return to the discussion of the model. Having defined transformation by means of the terms "S-structure" and "environment", we can work out some of the features of transformability. Suppose we know that, for a certain rearrangement, the requirement of semantic connection is fulfilled, but we do not know whether the

[1] partition

requirement of completeness is fulfilled. The following statement is an answer to the given question.

Theorem 5.7. If a rearrangement in a simple and formally homogeneous language satisfies the requirement of semantic connection, then it is a transformation.

This theorem shows that any reasonable rearrangement determined from the phrases of a homogeneous, simple language, is a transformation. In other words, the concepts of the LFT and of the homogeneous, simple language are extremely close to one another.

§47 · *On the compilation of a list of transformations applicable to actual languages*

We now recall how, in Chapter IV, we interpreted the process of forming environments. The process of compiling a list of transformations can, it seems, be envisaged in exactly the same way. Originally, the environments were only established on the basis of the unity of the semantic information. Further, we saw that one of the methods of raising the degree of homogeneity of a language consisted in redefining the environments. We divided the original establishment of the environments so that they came closer to the subenvironments (in the ideal case, they coincided with them). In this way, the environments were defined, taking account both of the semantic information (the original establishment) and also of the systemic relations in the language (a test for homogeneity).

We apply this procedure to the rearrangements which we wish to regard as transformations.

Consider two phrases A_1 and B_1 which, on the basis of an analysis of the environments, we assume to be in a state of transformability one to the other. It is obvious that there is no sense in introducing a transformation that only applies to one phrase of the given structure. We shall, therefore, ascertain how close the suggested transformation is to a complete one (whether, in the ideal case, it is one). We leave only those transformations that answer the given condition. In this way, we shall, in practice, be striving to the end that the transformation has a particular semantic invariant, and is fairly near to a complete one.

Care in the formulation of the rules of transformation and the requirement of bringing the practical concept of transformation close to what we had in the model are important, because, with a reasonable utilization of these concepts, it is possible to solve a whole series of linguistically important problems connected with the appeal to meaning. In Linguistics and Logic, the meaning of an utterance is often discussed without a precise definition of this concept. The presence of a full list of transformations for a given language (or sublanguage) enables us to define precisely what is meant by "Phrases A and B have *one and the same meaning*". It is possible to say that A and B have one and the same meaning if A can be considered as a chain of phrases C_1, C_2, ... C_n and B as a chain of phrases D_1, D_2, ... D_m, such that for each C_i there is a D_j in a relation of transformation with it, and for each D_k there is a D_l in a relation of transformation with it.

It is clear that an establishment of the formal rules for identity of meaning is important, both for theory and for application.

As an illustration of what significance this circumstance has for linguistic theory, let us pause to consider the question of syntactic homonyms and syntactic synonyms, that is, just those questions in which, not only the grammatical form, but also the meaning, is considered.

Definitions. 1) A construction A is a *syntactic homonym* if there exist two phrases different by structure of tree A_1 and A_2, such that A_1 has the same meaning as A, and A_2 has the same meaning as A.

2) Two constructions A_1 and A_2 are *syntactic synonyms* if there exists a phrase A having the same meaning as A_1 and the same meaning as A_2, and, in the configurational analysis, the two constructions A_1 and A_2 are configurations with the same resultant x.

Examples. The construction *otkrytie laboratorii*[1] is a syntactic homonym, as it can be represented as arising in the result of the transformations to completeness of two different phrases: "*Laboratoriya otkryla* (nechto)"[2]; "(*Nekto*) *otkryl laboratoriyu*"[3].

The constructions "(On rasskazal) o *priezde brata*"[4] and "(On rasskazal), *brat priekhal*"[5] are synonyms, as: 1) *priezd brata* → *brat priekhal* is a transformation near to completeness; 2) both constructions have the same distribution as, for instance, the word *eto*[6].

[1] [the] opening / of [the] laboratory
[2] [The] laboratory / opened / something.
[3] Somebody / opened / [the] laboratory.
[4] He / reported / on / [the] arrival / of [his] brother.
[5] He / reported / [his] brother / had arrived.   [6] this

These examples show convincingly enough the significance of Transformational Analysis (TA), which is connected with the fact that the idea of semantic invariance lies at its base. They show that TA promises to settle the cardinal problem in Linguistics, namely, the problem of meaning, which has, up to now, not yielded to solution owing to the lack of clarity of the ways of formalizing meaning. But, where there are no means of formalization, there is scope for any subjective structure. Only with the presence of clear formal rules for the establishment of identity of meaning is there a guarantee against subjectivism.

But it must be candidly admitted that precisely the idea of semantic invariance gives rise to some substantial difficulties in TA, some of which we consider later on.

At first glance, the rearrangements considered in TA differ little from the rearrangements considered in configurational analysis; it is permitted to replace a group of symbols, not by one resultant as in the preceding models, but by a group of symbols. There is, however, a considerable difference in how the configurations of symbols which are subject to replacement by the given symbols are defined. If configurational analysis is wholly constructed on the purely formal criterion of distribution, then distributional analysis can only be an auxiliary means for TA.

Since, in TA, the philologist is, as a rule, deprived of this most powerful formal criterion in establishing the rules of the rearrangement, then – if he disregards the criterion of completeness put forward in the model – he is left with only one course: to establish, by using his own linguistic intuition, that, in the given language, a chain of words A transforms into another chain B.

It is true that, in Phonology and Morphology, when a situation arises for which it is necessary to explain whether two words (groups of words) have exactly the same meaning, the philologist does not hesitate to turn to an informant with the question: do they mean one and the same thing or not? No philologist can dispense with this method in practice, especially in his own field-work.

There is, however, a fundamental difference between the application of this method in Phonology and in TA. First of all, it is usually emphasized that, in order to achieve objectivity, the question put to the informant must be of an indirect character. The informant must "answer the questions . . . about how something is said in his language, not about his language".[14] In particular, the most objective results are obtained by questions of the type: "Is the given phrase correctly constructed?" or more simply: "Do people speak like this?" The answer to the question as to whether two words have one and the same meaning or not may give very contradictory results indeed. If, however, this kind of question is asked in phonological research, then the possible subjectivity is not so dangerous, since the corresponding criterion in Phonology can be turned into a subsidiary one (or may disappear completely if the phoneme is defined purely distributively).

The situation is different in TA. Here the question whether phrases A and B mean one and the same thing is not an indirect one, but a direct question to be put directly "to someone's face". And so the danger of subjective arbitrariness is quite considerable. This difficulty could be overcome by subjecting the data of the questionnaire to statistical processing.

But, in TA, there is another difficulty too which cannot be eliminated by a similar statistical method. The fact is that, in complicated structures the constituent elements of which are transformed phrases, as a result of juxtaposition, there arise grammatical meanings not present in the initial phrases. We take the Russian gerundial expressions as an example, for instance,

Tak tyazhkii mlat, *drobya steklo*, kuet bulat[1]
(Pushkin).

If we ask an informant whether the words *mlat drobit steklo*[2] and *drobya steklo* mean exactly one and the same thing in this case, then we shall, most likely, get a negative reply. A more intelligent informant might say that, to a certain degree, "mlat *drobit steklo*" is only part of the meaning of the expression *drobya steklo*, that, in the expression, there is a concessive meaning, and that the expression is equivalent to the phrase "khotya on i *drobit steklo*"[3]. Such a reply doubtless pleases the philologist-researcher. But can we be sure that we shall always get it? It is enough to show the quoted phrase to ten different people to ascertain how varied is the information which we obtain in such cases. In the analysis of such phrases the philologist will obtain the most exact result if he relies on his own intuition.

[1] Thus / [the] heavy / hammer / shattering / [the] glass / forges / [the] blade.
[2] [The] hammer / shatters / [the] glass.
[3] although / it / also / shatters / [the] glass

It seems that both tasks – the definition of the invariance of meaning and the establishment of the rules of transformation – must be settled simultaneously. The establishment of the rules must stipulate our hypotheses, in this way exactifying our understanding of the semantic invariants of a given language, whereas the rules themselves must be confirmed by an analysis of the intrasystemic relations. It is just here that the requirement of closeness to a complete transformation is extremely important.

§48 · *Transformational synthesis*

The model of generation, considered in §44, consisted, as we may recall, in the establishment of certain basic structures and of certain rules of the type $x_i \rightarrow y_i$, where x_i always consisted of one symbol. We saw that this kind of model does not enable us to describe the facts of Language adequately.

Suppose that we have all the constructions from a language in the sense of §42, that is, S-structures in which all the attributes have been removed. We select the simplest of these constructions, for instance those corresponding to the phrases:

1) *Mal'chik idet*[1],
2) *Mal'chik beret knigu*[2],
3) *Mal'chik krasivyi*[3].

Chomsky called a set of similar phrases of very simple construction the *kernel of the language*. It is possible to consider that the remaining phrases are obtained from the kernel phrases by means of a combination of a method of development of phrases by the addition of attributes and of certain rearrangements which Chomsky called transformations, and which we shall, for the time being, call "free rearrangements". In a free rearrangement a chain of symbols $x_1, \ldots x_m$, is replaced by another chain $y_1, \ldots y_n$, where the number of such rearrangements must be finite.

For instance, from Phrases 1 and 2 one can obtain ones like:

1*a*) *Segodnya mal'chik idet v kino*[4] (by means of the replacement

[1] [The] boy / is walking.
[2] [The] boy / takes / [the] book.
[3] [The] boy / [is] / handsome.
[4] Today / [the] boy / is going / to / [the] cinema.

of *idet* by *idet segodnya* and *idet v kino* and the transformation *mal'chik idet segodnya* → *segodnya mal'chik idet*, where three elements are replaced at the same time);

2*a*) *Kniga beretsya mal'chikom*[1] (by means of a passive transformation where three elements are also replaced at once).

In generation, the rules of free rearrangement are established arbitrarily, i.e. no restrictions are placed on the rules for the replacement of one chain by another.

But the question arises How may the rules of free rearrangement be established more usefully?

First of all it is clear that it is unprofitable to establish these rules for individual phrases. We did indeed require that the number of rules of free rearrangement should be finite, but, naturally, we shall wish to generate an infinite set of phrases (cf. §43).

Hence it follows that rules need to be established for certain structures, and, as is clear from the discussion of §39, these structures must be complete.

Secondly, it follows from the examples quoted at the end of §45 that we shall wish our rearrangement to retain a particular semantic invariant.

From this it is clear that a free rearrangement can be constructed most usefully of all by making it correspond to the transformation of §46; we shall call *transformational synthesis* the method of generating by free rearrangements which is reciprocal to transformational analysis.

Here, it must be observed that we have in this work somewhat modified the exposition of the ideas of the transformational method in comparison with Chomsky's works. The transformational method was formulated by him, starting out from the idea of generation, i.e. methods were studied to discover how, given a particular stipulated phrase, one should reconstruct the process of its generation. In other words, the transformational method was conceived as a discriminating model in the sense of §4. It is clear, however, that the creation of a reasonable discriminating model presupposes the existence of good models of pure analysis and of pure synthesis. And so we have preferred to give detailed consideration to the analytic model and to explain transformational synthesis as a simple conversion of this analytic model.

[1] [The] book / is being taken / by [the] boy.

§49 · *The model of generation and the paradigmatic model*

We have considered a whole series of different models of Language. In this connection, the reader will, it appears, already have noticed that the models are being considered in an order which, in a definite sense, agrees with the tradition accepted in Linguistics: Phonology (the paradigmatics and syntagmatics of phonemes), Morphology (the paradigmatic relations in Grammar) and Syntax (the syntagmatic relations in Grammar).

It is important to explain now whether this order corresponds to the significance of the various linguistic phenomena from the point of view of the construction of a general model of the language habits of Man.

First of all, we observe that, recently, philologists and mathematicians occupied with the formal analysis of Language have paid much the most attention to synthetic or generative models, and this is understandable; the investigation of such models is explicitly (as in Chomsky's latest works) or implicitly connected with a definite hypothesis as to the process by which Man makes use of Language. It is just this process that is modelled by means of an automaton of the type investigated in §45 in connection with Yngve's hypothesis. In its general form this automaton can be defined as a system capable of generating definite successions of symbols. The most general type of such an automaton is a mechanism with an unrestricted storage capable of carrying out all the potentially realizable operations necessary for the generation of any previously established linear succession of symbols (such an automaton corresponds, it seems, to the so-called Turing's Machine).[15] It is clear that Man, having only a limited memory, must be modelled by an automaton on the activity of which a series of restrictions has been imposed. The most powerful of these restrictions changes such an automaton into a device generating a language with a finite number of states. Chomsky has shown that, between these two extreme types of automata, there can be placed all automata capable of producing a particular set of phrases.

The above point of view – which has been described – is doubtless exceedingly fruitful for the development of Linguistics and its associated disciplines, which have recently begun to make great use of cybernetic ideas (for instance, Psychology).

As we have seen, the construction of generative – that is synthetic – models is naturally bound up with an examination of analytic models, and, as well as this, every synthetic model can be constructed on the basis of some analytic model which assists us to understand the basic concepts and relations and gives us objective criteria for the establishment of the various rules of rearrangement (for instance, of the rules for the development of configurations or even of transformational rules). In the construction of analytic models the experience of Descriptive Linguistics can to a considerable extent be used for many concepts (for instance, "kernel", "satellite", "direct constituent", etc.) of which it is possible to construct a fairly natural analogue in terms of an analytic and then of a synthetic model also.

The fact that concepts that have been worked out in the process of development of one of the trends in Linguistics can be used in some model undoubtedly increases the discriminating value of the corresponding model.

While, however, we confirm the fruitfulness of the idea of Language being connected with the construction of an automaton of the type described above, it should all the same be observed that, if we reduce all the differences between the different models to certain restrictions on the character of the operations being performed by the automaton, we hardly come nearer to the creation of a model more or less adequately reflecting the Language behaviour of Man. It is significant that, with such an approach to making models of Language, there is no room left for all that which has been accumulated by the most recent European Philology, starting with the work of Baudouin de Courtenay and de Saussure, through the Prague Linguistic Circle, right up to the modern schools of European Structuralism.

The basic achievement of this tendency, it seems, lies in the understanding of Language as a "system" – a conception to the elaboration of which Soviet philologists, too, have made a considerable contribution.

The representatives of this tendency – whatever may be the differences between them – consider that the separate elements of Language enter into a complicated hierarchy of paradigmatic relations, the linguistic significance of a separate element being determined, not only by its place in a certain speech-succession, but also by the general character of the system, the presence or absence in it of other units, and by those intrasystemic relations the intersection of which is the given unit.

These considerations necessitate a more careful analysis of the hypothesis as to the generation of Language by an automaton which was described above.

In this hypothesis it has, apparently, up till now been implicitly assumed that one of two things happens:

a) the automaton consists only of a mechanism of generation and itself produces phrases according to its own programme;

b) the automaton processes phrases (that is, certain successions of signals) obtained from without.

In the models of generation which we are dealing with here only the first case is considered. And this is quite as expected, if we start out from the fact that, in the second case, the phrases being processed by the automaton are produced by some other automaton of the same form, the information only going in one direction, viz. from the automaton producing the phrases to the automaton which is processing them, and not being able to be created by the processing automaton. For, in this case, the uniting of two automata of the same form leads to a model which is isomorphous to the model of one automaton producing certain phrases arbitrarily. This can also be expressed somewhat differently. The hypothesis according to which the production of human speech can be modelled by an automaton of the type described above presupposes a passive processing of information in which there can only be produced a loss of the information, certainly not an enrichment of it.

Properly speaking, we have no direct proofs that the functional-ization of Language should be thought of otherwise. However, it is quite possible to think of another approach to making models in which, not only the restrictions connected with the character of the operations (the replacement of one chain of symbols by another) are investigated, but also certain hypotheses as to the internal structure of the automaton connected with the procedure of the active processing of information – the process of increasing the ex-tent of its organization – are formulated.

This more complicated model can be represented as consisting of two parts, an automaton which processes information, and a source of information; but, as distinct from the situation considered above, we are not making any hypotheses concerning the source of the information; rather, we presuppose that the processing auto-

maton accepts any information such as that which has been dis-
torted under the influence of noise – perhaps partly lost – or which
has a form totally unsuitable for processing.

In connection with this the processing automaton falls into two
parts, the mechanism of generation and the mechanism of ordering.
Schematically, this can be represented in the following way:

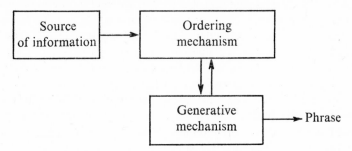

We shall consider that the ordering mechanism obtains information from the source, distributes it on the basis of certain criteria
into classes (for instance, categories, environments) and transmits
it to the generative mechanism, which, in its turn, transmits to the
ordering mechanism information about those elements which occupied the above-mentioned places in the sections of the phrase being
produced. This additional information makes possible the final
categorization (for instance, the choice of the families in our models).

It could also have been considered that the ordering mechanism
was associated by feed-back with the source of information too,
influencing, in fact, the character of the chain of symbols being produced by this source. Such an assumption is even essential in the
case that the automaton not only actively influences the information
being received but, at the same time, changes the surrounding
medium, as happens in the process of human work. But from the
point of view of making models, this, it seems, does not introduce
anything essentially new, and so we limit ourselves just to the
hypothesis of the active processing of information by some ordering
mechanism (this remark, however, does throw some light on the
process of secondary ordering – of which something below).

The mechanism which orders and enriches the information,
grouping it by definite categories membership of which, generally
speaking, is not established by its original form, would then correspond to the functioning of the paradigmatic system of a language.

At the same time, it can be conceived that the necessity of combating entropic tendencies[16] leads to the system of the various classes which assist in the ordering (in terms of our models "families", "environments", "categories"), itself, in its turn, being subjected to a strict ordering (such, for instance, is the tendency to "the homogeneity of Language").

It is necessary to note that this kind of secondary ordering is not, generally speaking, obligatory for the transmission of information, as it greatly increases redundancy (in the Information-Theory sense), but it can probably be explained by the general striving to overcome the entropic tendencies of the surrounding world. For it is this striving that is characteristic of all human activity. As we know, work, which played a decisive rôle in the bringing of Language into existence, is the basis of this activity. Thus, it is by no means essential that Language should function according to a model equipped with an ordering mechanism. There are, however, many indirect considerations which suggest that this model is closer to the actual functioning of Language than the one in which the information is processed passively, and, therefore, only the restrictions on the form of the operations are investigated. Indeed, the facts of the entirely different categorization of sections of operation in different languages prove that, in essence, not a single category is absolutely necessary. Thus, each of the categories of the noun in Russian which were examined by us is absent in some other language; gender is absent in English, Case and Number in Indonesian, and so on. Nevertheless there are no languages in which categories would be entirely absent. More than this, there are no languages where the categories would not form a definite harmonious system, fairly close to a "homogeneous" one. To explain the presence of categories only by the requirements of the limitation of rank (as we tried to do in connection with Yngve's hypothesis) is, in the general case, hardly likely to work.

As far as the secondary ordering within the system of categories itself is concerned, the fact of the isomorphism noted by us (or in any case the considerable similarity) between Phonology and Grammar confirms that the tendency towards systemicity is not something fortuitous or external.

It could be assumed that a system of ordering information has the same homeostatic properties (i.e. the tendency towards the conservation of internal stability[17]) as other systems assisting in the resistance of an organism to forces directed towards the increase of the general entropy of the surrounding medium.

In any case, we have seen that, starting from this kind of premise (which, admittedly, as we have already said, is not obligatory), it is possible to make a model of the formation process of individual paradigms, both in the course of learning a language and in the historical development of a language.

For the philologist, the basic advantage of a model equipped with a mechanism for ordering information is that, in such a model, there is wide scope for the use of the ideas and notions being developed by modern Linguistics, the cardinal concept of which, without doubt, is the concept of the "system" (the completely natural inclusion of Martinet's conceptions in the paradigmatic model may serve as an example of this).

Furthermore, the consideration of such a model will apparently help in making a model of the process of translation as a process of transition from one system of ordering to another.[18]

Finally, it may be hoped that this model will make possible the construction – on cybernetic bases – of a strict typology of languages which will be based on a consistent comparison of ordering mechanisms. It seems that it is possible to create a universal set of features, starting from which it is possible to obtain a very wide variety of categorization which takes into account the peculiarities of all the languages of the world. In any case, the study of differential marks at the different levels of Language, started at the present time, will doubtless help to make considerable progress in the investigation of the different classes of ordering mechanisms.

It is conceivable that the model which includes the mechanism of ordering corresponds more to the description of Language from the point of view of the associated disciplines – and also, above all, to Psychology.

If the first model to some extent reflects the atomizing approach of American behaviourism, with which Descriptive Linguistics is doubtless also connected, the second one corresponds, rather, to the modern tendency towards the study of "the whole" already initiated by the so-called Gestalt-psychology, which is to some extent near to the European structuralism of the thirties.

In any case it would be interesting to try to begin making models of generation with ordering mechanisms worked into them. Enthusiasm for "pure" models of generation has led to paradigmatic models being elaborated by no means as strictly and consistently as models of generation. More than this, the Theory of Sets conceptions which are the most suitable for the paradigmatic analysis of Language are not being developed as they should be.

Although we did not succeed in connecting the model of generation with the paradigmatic ones (the reader may perceive the first attempts in this direction in the section on Transformational Analysis and Transformational Synthesis), we nevertheless kept to that order of explaining the theory of Models of Language which corresponds to the need to investigate the paradigmatic models before constructing syntagmatic models, and, in particular, models of generation.

The traditional hierarchy of levels in Language intuitively reflects the significance of the separate parts, one for the other, which had been accurately guessed. We can indeed conceive of Syntax without Morphology, but this reduces its possibilities. Exactly similarly one can construct a morphology without reference to Syntagmatics, or to the Paradigmatics of the Phoneme. But the whole development of modern Philology shows that good morphology is unthinkable without phonology, and good syntax without morphology.

The scheme for making models of linguistic behaviour suggested is, of course, one-sided, since it does not take sufficient account of the communicative function of Language (which must be modelled by at least two automata transmitting information one to the other). However this would necessitate a widespread introduction of Information-Theory ideas into the making of models of Language, and this, in principle, is beyond the scope of our present work, in which only logical ("Set") and not statistical models of Language are examined.

AUTHOR'S FOOTNOTES

Chapter I

[1] *Kratkii kurs matematicheskogo analiza* 613.

[2] *Cours de linguistique générale* 154.

[3] See, for instance, G. Polya, *Mathematics and plausible reasoning*, vol I.

[4] "A mathematical representation (a model) of languages is by no means identical with the language itself" [Translation – *N.F.C.O. and A.S.C.R.*]; see N. D. Andreev and L. R. Zinder, *VYa* 1959, No. 4, p. 18.

[5] For the concept "construct", see S. K. Shaumyan, "Operatsionnye opredeleniya i ikh primenenie v Phonologii", *PL* 150-5.

[6] *Human knowledge: its scope and limits* 255-6.

[7] *ibid.* 258

[8] See A. A. Zinov'ev and I. I. Revzin, "Logicheskaya model' kak sredstvo nauchnogo poznaniya", *Voprosy Filosofii* 1960, No. 1, pp. 83-5.

[9] See Trubetzkoy 6-7.

[10] M. Joos, "Description of Language design", *Journal of the Acoustical Society of America* xxii, 701-8.

[11] Cf. Aristotle's remark as to the discrete nature of "Speech". [See J. L. Ackrill, *Aristotle's* Categories *and* De Interpretatione §4*b*.32-7 and note, p. 93 – *N.F.C.O. and A.S.C.R.*]

[12] See Greenberg.

[13] See Tseitin.

[14] Harris 7-9.

[15] See Chomsky.

[16] Jespersen 39-45.

[17] Shcherba 84 ff.

[18] V. Mathesius, *Obsahový rozbor současné angličtiny na základě obecně lingvistickém* 11-13.

[19] R. Jakobson and M. Halle, *Fundamentals of Language*.

[20] C. F. Hockett, "Two models of grammatical description", *Word* x, 210-34.

[21] Greenberg 7. His example is trivial, although it is easily grasped. In Linguistics, the possibility of a double description of one and the same phenomenon has already attracted attention; cf. Juen-Ren Chao, "The non-uniqueness of phonemic solutions of phonetic systems", M. Joos, *Readings in Linguistics* 38-54.

[22] In F. W. Harwood, "Axiomatic Syntax", *Language* xxxi, 409-13, the following estimates of the efficiency of a model are suggested (for the model of the first type, of §2). Let L be the Set of registered sequences and M the Set of unregistered sequences. Let C be the Set of sequences that can be generated by the model of the sequences, and D its supplement. Let LC be the intersection $L \cap C$, and MD the intersection $M \cap D$. We denote by $n(M)$, $n(L)$, $n(LC)$ and $n(MD)$

the number of sequences in the corresponding Set. Then it is possible to make the estimates

$$F = \frac{n(LC)}{n(L)} \text{ and } f = \frac{n(MD)}{n(M)}.$$

The ideal case is when $F = f = 1$, that is, when C coincides with L. When $n(M) = 0$ (i.e. when any sequences are registered), the unfavourable estimate is meaningless. The extreme case is $F = 1$, $f = 0$, i.e. when not all the sequences are registered, but they are all generated by the given model.

[23] Tseitin.

[24] Shcherba 74.

[25] T. M. Nikolaeva, "Opyt postroeniya algoritmicheskoi morfologii russkogo yazyka", *STI* i, 25-45.

[26] L. A. Chistovich, "Tekushchee raspoznavanie rechi chelovekom", *MP* vi.

[27] In this connection see Hill's reasonable objections to Chomsky's criterion of "grammaticality" ("Grammaticality", *Word* xvii, 1-10).

[28] See Vyach. Vs. Ivanov, "Tipologiya i sravnitel'no-istoricheskoe yazykoznanie", *VYa* 1958, No. 5, pp. 34-42; V. Skalička, "O současném stavu typologie", *Slovo a slovesnost* xix, 224-32; the same, "Z nové typologické literatury", *ibid.* xxi, 41-3.

[29] See M. I. Burlakova, T. M. Nikolaeva, D. M. Segal and V. N. Toporov, "Strukturnaya tipologiya i slavyanskoe yazykoznanie", *STI* i, 3-18.

[30] *Logique et analyse* II.ii, 29.

Chapter II

[1] For this concept, see P. S. Kuznetsov, "Ob opredelenii fonemy", *Byulleten'* v.

[2] For simplicity, we shall make use of the usual articulational perceptive marks, and not the acoustic marks described in R. Jakobson, G. M. Fant and M. Halle, *Preliminaries to Speech Analysis*; in some cases we shall indicate what changes are introduced by appealing to this system of marks.

[3] Cf. L. Yakubinskii's articles "O poeticheskom glossemosochetanii" and "Skoplenie odinakovykh plavnykh v prakticheskom i poeticheskom yazykakh", *Poetika: Sborniki po teorii poeticheskogo yazyka* i, 7-12, 50-7.

[4] Cf. Tolstoy's description of this process in "War and Peace" [*Voina i mir*, vol. IV, Part iv, chapter 9 (L. Tolstoy, *Polnoe sobranie sochinenii*, vol. XII (Moscow, 1940), p. 195 lines 29-34)]: " '*Vive Henri Quatre! Vive ce roi vaillant!*' sang Morel', winking. '*Ce diable à quatre . . . Vivarika! Vif seruvaru! sidyablika!*', repeated the soldier, waving his hand and really taking up the refrain." [Translation – N.F.C.O. and A.S.C.R.] It is interesting that, here, there are Russian phonetic words with unvoicing of voiced consonants at the absolute end (*vif*) and the transition of *e* to *i* in the pretonic position.

[5] Cf. I. I. Revzin, *Word* xix, 388-9.

[6] *TCLP* iv, 77.

[7] It is necessary, however, to mention L. Hjelmslev's interesting works in this direction: "La syllabation en slave" (*Zbornik* 315-24) and "The syllable as a structural unit", *Proceedings of the Third international Congress of Phonetic Science* 266-72.

[8] R. I. Avanesov, "Kratchaishaya zvukovaya edinitsa v sostave slova i morfemy", *VG* 119 ff.

⁹ See L. R. Zinder, "Spetsificheskie osobennosti vospriyatiya zvukov rechi", *Vospriyatie zvukovykh signalov v razlichnykh akusticheskikh usloviyakh* 69-73 (esp. p. 70).

¹⁰ See Trubetzkoy 71.

¹¹ R. I. Avanesov, *Fonetika sovremennogo russkogo literaturnogo yazyka* 31 ff.

¹² See E. C. Cherry, "Roman Jakobson's 'Distinctive Features' as the normal co-ordinates of a language", *For Roman Jakobson* 60-4.

¹³ See Martinet 73-5.

¹⁴ The first figure indicates the number of the Chapter, the second the ordinal number of the theorem in the given Chapter (for the proofs of this and the succeeding theorems, see the *Appendix*).

¹⁵ For the importance of the principle of Fullness, the first indications of which are already in Baudouin de Courtenay, see V. N. Toporov, *I. A. Boduen de Kurtene* 35.

¹⁶ Martinet, Chapter III "Structure".

¹⁷ Martinet 66.

¹⁸ See Siebs, *Deutsche hochsprache, Bühnenaussprache*.

¹⁹ See W. Neumann, *Sprachpflege* iv, 71.

²⁰ See, for instance, S. K. Shaumyan, *Istoriya sistemy differentsial'nykh elementov v pol'skom yazyke* 75-6; L. E. Kalnyn', *Razvitie korrelyatsii tverdykh i myagkikh soglasnykh fonem v slavyanskikh yazykakh* 64, 67-8.

²¹ See Z. Stieber, "Über das gegenseitige verhältnis der heutigen polnischen phoneme *s − š* und *z − ž*", *Die welt der Slaven* ii, 121-4.

²² N. S. Trubetzkoy, *Altkirchenslavische grammatik* 78.

²³ Trubetzkoy 219-20.

²⁴ Bloch and Trager, *Outline of Linguistic Analysis*.

²⁵ See F. Harary and H. H. Paper, "Toward a general calculus of phonemic distribution", *Language* xxxiii, 143-69; B. Sigurd, "Rank order of consonants established by distributional criteria", *Studia linguistica* ix, 8-20; L. Gårding, "Relations and order", *ibid.* ix, 21-34; E. Vasiliu, "Une classification des consonnes roumaines d'après le critère de la distribution", *Mélanges* 97-112. Henceforth we shall rely on the first work; for the general theory of ratios, see A. Tarski, *Introduction to Logic and to the methodology of deductive sciences* 87-116.

²⁶ Cf. the ideas as to this question in R. T. Harms' dissertation, *A descriptive grammar of Estonian* 38-9.

²⁷ Harary and Paper, *op. cit.*

²⁸ "Energiebasis − Artikulationsbasis", *Wiener slavistisches jahrbuch* vi, 93-7.

²⁹ S. Marcus and E. Vasiliu, "La théorie des graphes et le consonantisme de la langue roumaine", *Revue de mathématiques pures et appliquées* v, 319-40.

³⁰ In the work mentioned, Marcus and Vasiliu call phonemes reconstructed in this way *redundant*. In actual fact, there is some connection between the problem of Redundancy as it is posed in modern Information Theory and as it is considered by us. But we should prefer not to use the term "Redundancy" in this connection.

³¹ Results of R. L. Dobrushin's experiments in A. M. Yaglom and I. M. Yaglom, *Veroyatnost' i informatsiya* 192 ff. (see also *MatP* vi, 48-9).

³² The corresponding probabilities have been calculated for combinations of two sounds by R. L. Zinder; see *Voprosy Statistiki Rechi* 58-61.

Chapter III

[1] H. Frei, "Critères de délimitation", *Word* x, 136-45.

[2] See Trubetzkoy.

[3] Cf., for instance, A. N. Gvozdev, "O predelakh deistviya zvukovykh zakonomernostei v russkom yazyke" (*O fonologicheskikh sredstvakh russkogo yazyka* 84-97).

[4] See, in particular, Bally 330-40, where the facts of French and German are consistently compared.

[5] See I. I. Revzin, "O logicheskoi forme lingvisticheskikh opredelenii", *PL* 140-8.

[6] For the linguistic significance of the parameters in Zipf's Formula, see, for instance, R. M. Frumkina, "K voprosu o tak nazyvaemom 'zakone Tsipfa'", *VYa* 1961, No. 2, p. 118 ff.; see also D. M. Segal, "Nekotorye utochneniya veroyatnostoi modeli Tsipfa", *MP* v, 51-5.

[7] E. Sapir, *Language*, Chapter VI.

[8] J. H. Greenberg, "A quantitative approach to the morphological typology of languages", *International Journal of American Linguistics* xxvi, 178-94.

[9] *TCLP* iv, 190.

[10] See R. P. Stockwell, "The place of intonation in a generative grammar of English", *Language* xxxvi, 360-7.

[11] See A. A. Reformatskii, *Vvedenie v yazykoznanie*.

[12] See Chomsky; see also the review by E. V. Paducheva, *VYa* 1959, No. 1, pp. 133-8.

[13] B. Bloch, *Language* xxvi, 88.

[14] A. A. Kholodovich, "Opyt teorii podklassov slov", *VYa* 1960, No. 1, pp. 32-43.

[15] These concepts, like the majority of those used further on, were formulated by A. A. Lyapunov and O. S. Kulagina (see Kulagina).

[16] The idea of "completeness" is due to Greenberg; admittedly, he uses the term "complete construction" (more accurately, "subconstruction"), but this does not change the essentials of the matter.

[17] K. Bühler, *TCLP* vi, 10.

[18] See E. Haugen, *Language* xxvii, 213 ff.

[19] See, for instance, C. F. Voegelin, "Linguistics without meaning and culture without words", *Word* v, 40 ff.

[20] See Vyach, Vs. Ivanov, "O postroenii informatsionnogo yazyka dlya tekstov po deskriptivnoi lingvistike" in *Doklady* vii.

[21] *Izbrannye trudy* 35.

[22] See G. Ryle, "Categories", *Logic and Language* ii, 66-7.

[23] E. Husserl, *Logische untersuchungen* II.i (2nd ed.); 294-5, 305-12, 316-21, 326-42.

[24] "Die syntaktische konnexität", *Studia philosophica* (*Commentarii Societatis philosophicae Polonorum*) i, 1-27.

[25] R. Carnap, *Meaning and necessity* 23-32; see also the references there to other works in which the problem of the substitutability of words is posed.

[26] We recall that a *phrase* is any succession of words, and, for instance, any part of a normal sentence is also a phrase. Finally, for generality, it is convenient to consider that a phrase can be empty, i.e. it does not contain a single word.

[27] See Uspenskii.

[28] V. A. Uspenskii, "K opredeleniyu padezha po Kolmogorovu", *Byulleten'* v, 22-6.

[29] See the analysis of the various points of view in Vinogradov i.

[30] Cf. the concept of the primary syntactic function introduced by J. Kuryłowicz ("Dérivation lexicale et dérivation syntaxique: Contribution à la théorie des parties du discours", *Bulletin de la Société de Linguistique de Paris* xxxvii, 79-92).

[31] A. M. Peshkovskii, *Sbornik statei* 131.

[32] *Zbornik* 16.

[33] It seems that an idea of I. A. Mel'chuk's is very helpful in deciding what should be regarded as grammatical and what as ungrammatical. He suggested calling "grammatical in a given language" a meaning that is obligatorily expressed in the given language that is, the words of the corresponding classes are unthinkable without the indicators of this meaning. Moreover, a supplementary requirement is also put forward, namely, that there should exist at least one language where this meaning is not expressed. (I. A. Mel'chuk, "K voprosu o grammaticheskom v yazyke-posrednike", *Tezisy* 1959, pp. 60-3.) In what follows, only those categories which I. A. Mel'chuk called "morphological" are examined, and so, in our work, the term "morphological category" will not be used in a narrower meaning.

[34] Peshkovskii 53-61.

[35] The concept of the elementary grammatical category corresponds to the concept "elementary information" introduced in Fitialov. The term "elementary grammatical category" was used in a somewhat different sense by R. L. Dobrushin (for this, see §32).

[36] For details of the categories "animate" and "inanimate", see §29.

[37] Cf. J. Kuryłowicz, "La notion d'isomorphisme", *Travaux du cercle linguistique de Copenhague* v, 56 ff.

[38] Here some ideas have been used which were put forward by Vyach. Vs. Ivanov and P. S. Kuznetsov at a seminar on Mathematical Linguistics in Moscow State University in the academic year 1957-8.

[39] Trnka 865-6.

[40] See E. V. Cheshko, *Osnovnye voprosy grammatiki bolgarskogo yazyka* 25, 43.

[41] R. Jakobson, "Beitrag zur allgemeinen kasuslehre", *TCLP* vi, 240-87.

[42] R. Jakobson, *Shifters, verbal categories and the Russian verb.*

[43] Cf. also R. Jakobson, "Morfologicheskie nablyudeniya nad slavyanskim skloneniem", *American contributions to the fourth International Congress of Slavicists* 127-56.

[44] Vyach. Vs. Ivanov, "Ponyatie neitralizatsii v morfologii i leksike", *Byulleten'* v, 56 ff.

Chapter IV

[1] See Kulagina.

[2] At least if we restrict ourselves to words in their "primary" function (cf. §24). It is clear that verbal nouns which retain the verbal government fall into special "parts of speech", different from the "part of speech" which includes the words *stol*[1], *okno*[2], *miska*[3], etc., since, for instance, in the phrase "*ovladenie znaniyami*"[4], the word *ovladenie* cannot be replaced by the word *okno*.

[3] This and the further definitions and statements of this paragraph are taken from Uspenskii.

[4] Peshkovskii 60.

[5] *VYa* 1960, No. 6, p. 93.

[6] "Lichnyi rod v pol'skom i rumynskom yazykakh", *RevL* v, 147-60.

[1] table   [2] window   [3] basin   [4] acquiring / skills

[7] See K. Pătrut, "Sur le genre 'neutre' en roumain", *Mélanges* 291-301.

[8] Cf. Theorems 2 and 3 in Kulagina.

[9] See Vinogradov ii, 380-90.

[10] P. S. Kuznetsov, *Razvitie indoevropeiskogo skloneniya v obshcheslavyanskom yazyke* 7.

[11] *ibid.* 49.

[12] For the concepts, "stability" and "perturbation", see Ashby, Chapter V.

[13] P. S. Kuznetsov, *VG* 114.

[14] Peshkovskii, Chapter I ("Ponyatie o forme slova").

[15] In this connection the model suggested by N. D. Andreev, which successfully combines statistical methods with an apparatus of the Theory of Sets conception of Language, is very interesting; see N. D. Andreev, "Modelirovanie yazyka na baze ego statisticheskoi i teoretiko-mnozhestvennoi struktury", *Tezisy* 1959, pp. 15-22.

[16] It is clear that the morphological division proceeds more naturally on the phonetic level, but, here, we are only interested in the general principle.

[17] R. L. Dobrushin, "Elementarnaya grammaticheskaya kategoriya", *Byulleten'* v, 19-20.

[18] *Prolegomena to a Theory of Language* 87 ff.

[19] See Trnka.

[20] This question is analysed in detail in S. Stati, "Omonimiya v morfologicheskoi sisteme", *RevL* v, 257-63.

[21] L. Hjelmslev, *La catégorie des cas* (*Acta jutlandica* VII.i), 81.

[22] This becomes clear from the following argument. This sort of distribution of forms into environments can be expressed thus: $S(b) = S(f)$; $S(d) \to S(a)$ and $S(c) \to S(e)$ in the terms of our abstract system. Under these conditions, as can easily be verified, neither $S(a) \to S(e)$ nor $S(e) \to S(a)$ can apply. Suppose, for instance, $S(a) \to S(e)$. Then (by Transitivity) $S(d) \to S(e)$, but this can only happen when e can everywhere stand in place of d. But we assumed that d and e were different word-forms.

[23] R. L. Dobrushin, "Matematicheskie metody v lingvistike", *MatP* vi, 52-9.

[24] See Fitialov.

[25] P. Sgall, "Soustava pádových koncovek v češtině", *Acta Universitatis Carolinae: Philologica* ii, 65-84.

[26] The term "type-form" has been borrowed from A. I. Smirnitskii (*VG* 36).

Chapter V

[1] See Kulagina.

[2] It is true that in H. A. Gleason's book *An introduction to Descriptive Linguistics* a construction is defined as "any significant group of words" (132), but it is quite simple to give the distributive analogue of this concept.

[3] See Jespersen, Chapter VII.

[4] de Groot, *Strukturelle syntaxis*; the same, "Structural Linguistics and syntactic laws", *Word* v, 1-12.

[5] Harris 265-8.

[6] See, for instance, R. S. Pittman, "Nuclear structures in Linguistics", *Language* xxiv, 287-92.

[7] See V. G. Admoni, *Vvedenie v sintaksis sovremennogo nemetskogo yazyka* 102 ff.

⁸ "A model and an hypothesis for Language Structure", *Proceedings of the American Philosophical Society* civ, 444-66.

⁹ G. A. Miller, "Human memory and the storage of information", *IRE Transactions on Information Theory*, vol. *IT*-2, No. 3, pp. 129-37.

¹⁰ It should be emphasized that the terms "progressive" and "regressive structure" are here used in a much narrower sense than are, for instance, "progressive" and "regressive succession", Bally 173-281.

¹¹ Point *b* of the First Condition corresponds to the condition of transformation put forward, V. V. Borodin, *Doklady* vi, 5.

¹² See H. Paul, *Deutsche grammatik* 74.

¹³ *VYa* 1958, No. 1, p. 77.

¹⁴ Harris 14.

¹⁵ See the description of "Turing's Machine", B. A. Trakhtenbrot, *Algoritmy i mashinnoe reshenie zadach* 62-100.

¹⁶ See N. Wiener, *The human use of human beings* 32-62.

¹⁷ For details of the concept "homeostat", see Ashby 83-5.

¹⁸ See I. I. Revzin and V. Yu. Rozentsvreig, "K obosnovaniyu lingvisticheskoi teorii perevoda", *VYa* 1962, No. 1, pp. 51-9.

APPENDIX

Chapter II §13*

Lemma Two different phonemes cannot have more than one common archiphoneme.

This follows immediately from the definition of the archiphoneme.

Theorem 2.1. If a subsystem does not contain empty cells, it is phonologically homogeneous.

Proof. Let $z \in K^{(1)}(x) \cap K^{(2)}(y)$. This means that z and x have a common archiphoneme α and can be represented in the form

$$x = \alpha \cup m_i, \tag{1}$$
$$z = \alpha \cup m_j. \tag{2}$$

Similarly, y and z have a common archiphoneme β $(\alpha \neq \beta)$ and can be represented in the form

$$y = \beta \cup l_i, \tag{3}$$
$$z = \beta \cup l_j. \tag{4}$$

From (2) and (4) it follows that $l_j \in \alpha$ and $m_j \in \beta$. In other words, $\alpha = \alpha' \cup l_j$ and $\beta = \beta' \cup m_j$.

$$z = \alpha' \cup l_j \cup m_j = \beta' \cup m_j \cup l_j \tag{5}$$

Put $\alpha' = \beta' = \gamma$ and rewrite equations (1)-(4) in the form

$$x = \gamma \cup l_j \cup m_i \tag{1a}$$
$$z = \gamma \cup l_j \cup m_j \tag{2a}$$
$$y = \gamma \cup l_i \cup m_j. \tag{3a}$$

Form a phoneme $w = \gamma \cup l_i \cup m_i$ (by the Condition l_i and l_j are fully homogeneous). Since in the division $K^{(1)}$ x and z fall into one class, y and w also fall into one class $K^{(1)}(y) = K^{(1)}(w)$, since they have the common archiphoneme $\gamma \cup l_i$; and, furthermore, w and x

* [A heading of this *Appendix* is the chapter and paragraph to which the section following it is relevant; thus "II §13" refers to Chapter II, Paragraph 13 – and so on. – *N.F.C.O. and A.S.C.R.*]

have the common archiphoneme $\gamma \cup m_i$, and z and y have the common archiphoneme $\gamma \cup m_j$. Thus $w \in K^{(1)}(y)$. Similarly it may be proved that $w \in K^{(2)}(x)$. Hence it follows that $K^{(1)}(y) \cap K^{(2)}(x)$ is non-empty. The Theorem is proved.

Theorem 2.2. If a subsystem is phonologically homogeneous, then two regular classes of one division cannot contain a different number of phonemes.

Proof. Let two classes $K^{(1)}(x)$ and $K^{(1)}(y)$ in the given division contain a non-identical number of phonemes:

$$K^{(1)}(x) = \{x_1, x_2, \ldots x_n\},$$
$$K^{(1)}(y) = \{y_1, y_2, \ldots y_m\},$$

and, for preciseness, suppose $n > m$. Note that, if we prove our statement for the case that a certain member of $K^{(1)}(x)$, for instance x_1, has a common archiphoneme with a member of $K^{(1)}(y)$, for instance y_1, then it automatically extends to the general case, for any two classes of the given division (according to construction) can be connected by a chain of classes, each pair of which satisfies the relation stated. And so we consider our special case. In a division $K^{(2)}$, x_1 and y_1 belong to one class. In this division, since there are more x's, and x_i and x_j cannot belong together to $K^{(2)}(y)$, there is an x_i such that $y_i \in K^{(2)}(x_i)$ does not exist. To be precise, let x_n be such an x. Then

$$K^{(2)}(x_n) \cap K^{(1)}(y_1) = 0.$$

At the same time

$$K^{(1)}(x_n) \cap K^{(2)}(y_1) = x_1.$$

Hence it follows that the language is not phonologically homogeneous. The Theorem is proved.

Theorem 2.3. If a system is phonologically homogeneous, and x constitutes an isolated class in the division $K^{(1)}$, and $y \in K^{(0)}(x)$, where $K^{(0)}$ is the initial division, then $K^{(1)}(y)$ is an isolated class.

Proof. Let $K^{(1)}(x)$ be an isolated class. By the Condition, there exists a y such that $y \in K^{(0)}(x)$. We show that $K^{(1)}(y)$ is an isolated class. Assume the opposite. Let $z \in K^{(1)}(y)$. Then $y \in (K^{(1)}(z) \cap K^{(0)}(x))$ and, because of the phonological homogeneity, there must be a phoneme w such that $w \in (K^{(1)}(x) \cap K^{(0)}(z))$. Hence, since $K^{(1)}(x)$ is an isolated class, $w = x$ and $z \in K^{(0)}(x)$. Hence $z \in K^{(0)}(y)$ and z and y have two different common archiphonemes: α, which defines the division $K^{(0)}$ and β, which defines the division $K^{(1)}$; and, by the Lemma on p. 172, this is impossible. The theorem is proved.

Theorem 2.4. In a phonologically homogeneous subsystem two adjacent phonemes have the same rank.

Proof. Let x_1 and y_1 be two adjacent phonemes; let y_1, x_2, x_3, $\ldots x_{m-1}$ (I) be all the phonemes adjacent to x_1; and x_1, y_2, y_3, $\ldots y_{n-1}$ (II) be all the phonemes adjacent to y_1 ($n > m$).

We shall say that y_j ($2 \le j \le n-1$) *stands in a relation of correlation with* x_i ($2 \le i \le m-1$) *in respect of the pair* (x_1, y_1), if for a certain two different divisions k and l, $x_1 \in K^{(k)}(y_1) \cap K^{(l)}(x_i)$ and $y_j \in K^{(k)}(x_i) \cap K^{(l)}(y_1)$.

If we prove that for every x_i there is one and only one y_j (and, conversely, that for every y_j there is one and only one x_i) satisfying these conditions, then from this it will follow that it is possible to establish a one-one correspondence between (I) and (II), and this will mean that $m = n$, and the Theorem will have been proved.

Consider now x_i ($2 \le i \le m-1$); x_i and x_1 have the common archiphoneme α, which defines a certain division $K^{(l)}$; and $x_1 \in K^{(l)}(x_i)$.

Furthermore, x_1 has an archiphoneme common with y_1. If this archiphoneme is α, x_i is a phoneme adjacent to y_1, that is, x_i is equal to one from y_j. We simply place such elements in correspondence with themselves. Now let x_1 and y_1 have the common archiphoneme β ($\beta \ne \alpha$), which defines the division $K^{(k)}$, that is $x_1 \in K^{(k)}(y_1) \cap K^{(l)}(x_i)$. By the condition of homogeneity there must exist a phoneme $z \in K^{(k)}(x_i) \cap K^{(l)}(y_1)$. Since $z \in K^{(l)}(y_1)$, z is adjacent to the phoneme y_1. If $z = y_1$, then $x_i \in K^{(k)}(x_1)$, and this is inconsistent with the Lemma on p. 172. If $z = x_1$, then $z \in K^{(k)}(y_1) \cap K^{(l)}(y_1)$, but this cannot be so, for we assumed that α and β were different archiphonemes. And so $z = y_j$ ($2 \le j \le n-1$) and y_j is in a relation of correlation with x_i in respect of the pair (x_1, y_1). Let there now be two different phonemes z' and z'' in a relation of correlation with x_i in respect of the pair (x_1, y_1). In that case the following relations arise:

$$z' \in K^{(k)}(x_i) \cap K^{(l)}(y_1),$$
$$z'' \in K^{(k)}(x_i) \cap K^{(l)}(y_1).$$

Hence it follows that z' and z'' belong to the same class in the division $K^{(k)}$ and to the same class in the division $K^{(l)}$; but this cannot be so, by the Lemma on p. 172.

Similarly it may be proved that for every phoneme y_j there is only one phoneme x_i which is in a relation of correlation with y_j in respect of the pair (x_1, y_1).

In this way one phoneme from (II) is placed in correspondence with each phoneme from (I) and conversely. The Theorem is proved.

Theorem 2.5. If a subsystem is full and phonologically homogeneous, it does not contain empty cells.

Proof. Suppose the conditions of the Theorem are fulfilled and let there be marks m_i and m_j such that for an archiphoneme α both $\alpha \cup m_i$ and $\alpha \cup m_j$ are phonemes. Furthermore, let there be a phoneme $\beta \cup m_i$, but let the phoneme $\beta \cup m_j$ be absent (in place of it there being an empty cell). Let $\alpha = a \cup \lambda$, $\beta = b \cup \lambda$, that is, we shall assume from the start that we have three phonemes which differ mutually by only one mark:

$$F_1 = a \cup \lambda \cup m_i;$$
$$F_2 = a \cup \lambda \cup m_j,$$
$$F_3 = b \cup \lambda \cup m_i.$$

F_1 and F_2 belong to one class in the division defined by the archiphoneme α. Let this be $K^{(1)}(F_1) = K^{(1)}(F_2)$. F_1 and F_3 belong to one class in the division defined by the archiphoneme $m_i \cup \lambda$. Let this be $K^{(2)}(F_1) = K^{(2)}(F_3)$. By the condition of homogeneity there must exist a phoneme F_4 which belongs to $K^{(1)}(F_3)$ and to $K^{(2)}(F_2)$. Let this phoneme have the form

$$F_4 = x \cup \lambda \cup y.$$

F_4 must have a common archiphoneme with F_2. Hence, for one of the elements x or y – suppose it be for x – it is true that $x = a$ or $x = m_j$. But, if $x = a$, then F_4 has a common archiphoneme with F_1, which is impossible. So

$$F_4 = m_j \cup \lambda \cup y.$$

Since F_4 must have a common archiphoneme with F_3, $y = m_i$ or $y = b$. The first is impossible, as homogeneous marks are inconsistent. So

$$F_4 = m_j \cup \lambda \cup b = \beta \cup m_j,$$

and the statement as to the absence of $\beta \cup m_j$ is disproved. Now let the phonemes F_1 and F_3 differ by k marks and consider the Theorem proved for phonemes which differ by $k-1$ marks.

Then there exist three phonemes:

$$F_1 = m_i \cup w \cup a_1 \cup a_2 \cup \ldots \cup a_k,$$
$$F_2 = m_j \cup w \cup a_1 \cup a_2 \cup \ldots \cup a_k,$$
$$F_3 = m_i \cup w \cup b_1 \cup b_2 \cup \ldots \cup b_k.$$

We shall suppose that there exists no phoneme

$$F_4 = m_j \cup w \cup b_1 \cup b_2 \cup \ldots \cup b_k.$$

By the condition of fullness there exists a phoneme F_3' such that F_3 differs from F_3' by one mark and from F_1 by $k-1$ marks.

By the inductive assumption, from the existence of F_1, F_2 and F_3' of form

$$F_3' = m_i \cup w \cup a_1 \cup b_2 \cup b_3 \cup \ldots \cup b_k,$$

there follows the existence of F_4' of form

$$F_4' = m_j \cup w \cup a_1 \cup b_2 \cup b_3 \cup \ldots \cup b_k.$$

And if F_3', F_4' and F_3 differ mutually by only one mark, then, as we have proved, there must exist a phoneme F_4 of form

$$F_4 = m_j \cup w \cup b_1 \cup b_2 \cup \ldots \cup b_k.$$

The Theorem is proved.

Lemma. Let $x \in K^{(i)}(y)$; then, for any j $(j \neq i)$, $x \bar{\in} K^{(j)}(y)$.

Let $x \in K^{(i)}(y)$ and $x \in K^{(j)}(y)$. Consider the first class of the j-division, $K_1^{(j)}$. The pair of phonemes (x, y) can be connected by a chain of pairs with a pair of phonemes (z, w) which belongs to $K_1^{(j)}$, it being given that, for adjacent pairs of chains, it is true that two phonemes within a pair have an archiphoneme in common, and that, for each phoneme of a pair, there exists a phoneme in another pair which has an archiphoneme in common with it. It may be proved by induction along this chain that $z \in K^{(i)}(w)$, and this contradicts point 4 of our edifice.

Corollary. Any archiphoneme defines a division uniquely.

Chapter IV §27

Theorem 4.1. (Kulagina's Theorem). For any x it is true that $B^*(x) = B^{**}(x)$.

Before we prove this theorem we introduce some auxiliary concepts (which we shall also need further on).

Consider two divisions of the set Ξ, namely $B^{(1)}$ and $B^{(2)}$.

We shall say that Division $B^{(1)}$ is *larger than* Division $B^{(2)}$ – alternatively that $B^{(1)}$ is an *extension* of Division $B^{(2)}$ – if $B^{(1)}(x) \supseteq B^{(2)}(x)$, all $x \in \Xi$, where $B^{(1)}$ and $B^{(2)}$ are not identical.

We shall say that Division $B^{(1)}$ is a *regular extension* of $B^{(2)}$ if from the Condition $B^{(2)}(y) \subseteq B^{(1)}(x)$ it follows that $B^{(2)}(y) \underset{B^{(2)}}{\sim} B^{(2)}(x)$, in other words, if each set of Division $B^{(1)}$ is the sum of the elements of Division $B^{(2)}$ which are $B^{(2)}$-equivalent among themselves. For instance, the derivative division is a particular case of regular extension. First of all we prove a number of auxiliary statements.

Lemma 1. Let $B^{(1)}$ be a regular extension of $B^{(2)}$, and let a particular $B^{(1)}$-structure correspond to a particular $B^{(2)}$-structure (it corresponds in the sense that $B_i^{(2)} \subseteq B_i^{(1)}$, where i is the place-number of an element of the given division in the structure). Then the unregistered $B^{(2)}$-structure cannot correspond to the registered $B^{(1)}$-structure.

Proof. Let the registered $B^{(1)}$-structure have the form

$$B^{(1)}(x_1)\, B^{(1)}(x_2) \ldots B^{(1)}(x_n), \tag{1}$$

where $A = x_1 x_2 \ldots x_n$ was that registered phrase which led to the registration of Structure (1).

Consider the $B^{(2)}$-structure of this phrase:

$$B^{(2)}(x_1)\, B^{(2)}(x_2) \ldots B^{(2)}(x_n). \tag{2}$$

It is, of course, registered. But in the Lemma it is assumed that there exists at least one such $B^{(2)}$-structure as

$$B^{(2)}(u_1)\, B^{(2)}(u_2) \ldots B^{(2)}(u_n), \tag{3}$$

which, on the one hand, is not registered, and, on the other hand, consists of $B_i^{(2)}$ such that $B_i^{(2)} \subseteq B_i^{(1)}$.

Since $B^{(1)}$ is a regular extension of $B^{(2)}$, $B^{(2)}(x_i) \underset{B^{(2)}}{\sim} B^{(2)}(u_i)$. This means that, substituting $B^{(2)}(x_1)$ for $B^{(2)}(u_1)$ in (3), we should once again have obtained an unregistered structure. If we carry out this substitution n times, we must once again obtain an unregistered structure. In actual fact, by this substitution, we pass from (3) to (2). So (2) is at the same time both a registered and an unregistered structure.

The contradiction that has resulted proves the Lemma.

ML N

Lemma 2. Let $B^{(1)}$ be a regular extension of $B^{(2)}$. Then from $B^{(2)}(x) \underset{B^{(2)}}{\sim} B^{(2)}(y)$ there follows $B^{(1)}(x) \underset{B^{(1)}}{\sim} B^{(1)}(y)$ and from $B^{(1)}(x) \underset{B^{(1)}}{\sim} B^{(1)}(y)$ there follows $B^{(2)}(u) \underset{B^{(2)}}{\sim} B^{(2)}(w)$ for any u and w such that $B^{(2)}(u) \subseteq B^{(1)}(x)$ and $B^{(2)}(w) \subseteq B^{(1)}(y)$.

Proof. We prove the first statement. Assume that $B^{(1)}(x)$ is not $B^{(1)}$-equivalent to $B^{(1)}(y)$ under the conditions of the Lemma, that is, there exist two phrases such as

$$A = x_1 x_2 \ldots x_{i-1} x x_{i+1} \ldots x_n$$

and

$$A' = x_1 x_2 \ldots x_{i-1} y x_{i+1} \ldots x_n,$$

and that, of the $B^{(1)}$-structures $B^{(1)}(A)$ and $B^{(1)}(A')$, one is registered and the other not, at the same time as $B^{(2)}(A)$ and $B^{(2)}(A')$ are simultaneously registered or not registered. Let $B^{(1)}(A)$ be registered, so that, by Lemma 1, $B^{(2)}(A)$ is also registered. Hence, by the Condition, $B^{(2)}(A')$ is also registered. By Lemma 1, $B^{(1)}(A')$ must also be a registered structure – but we assumed that it was not registered. Consequently we have arrived at a contradiction. The first part of the statement is proved.

We prove the second part of the statement. Let the $B^{(2)}$-structure:

$$B^{(2)}(A_1) \, B^{(2)}(u) \, B^{(2)}(A_2), \tag{1}$$

where $B^{(2)}(u) \subseteq B^{(1)}(x)$, be registered.

From the registration of (1) it follows that the $B^{(1)}$-structure:

$$B^{(1)}(A_1) \, B^{(1)}(x) \, B^{(1)}(A_2) \tag{2}$$

is also registered. Then, by the Condition of the Lemma, the $B^{(1)}$-structure:

$$B^{(1)}(A_1) \, B^{(1)}(y) \, B^{(1)}(A_2) \tag{3}$$

is also registered. Consider now the $B^{(2)}$-structure:

$$B^{(2)}(A_1) \, B^{(2)}(w) \, B^{(2)}(A_2), \tag{4}$$

where $B^{(2)}(w) \subseteq B^{(1)}(x)$. Since $B^{(1)}$ is a regular extension of $B^{(2)}$, (4) must be registered, by Lemma 1. Thus we can see that, from the registration of (1), there always follows the registration of (4). By a similar route it may be shown that, from the registration of (4) for arbitary u and w, there follows the registration of (1). And this proves the Lemma.

Lemma 3. Let $B^{(1)}$ be a regular extension of $B^{(2)}$. Then, for any x, $B^{(1)}*(x) = B^{(2)}*(x)$ – in other words, in a regular extension, the derivative division by $B^{(1)}$ coincides with the derivative division by $B^{(2)}$.

Proof. Consider $x \in B^{(2)}*(y)$. We prove that $x \in B^{(1)}*(y)$. By Lemma 2, $B^{(1)}(x) \underset{B^{(1)}}{\sim} B^{(1)}(y)$, that is, $x \in B^{(1)}(y)$. So we have proved that

$$B^{(2)}*(x) \subseteq B^{(1)}*(x). \tag{1}$$

Now let $x \in B^{(1)}*(y)$. We prove that $x \in B^{(2)}*(y)$. So, $B^{(1)}(x) \underset{B^{(1)}}{\sim} B^{(1)}(y)$. By Lemma 2 it follows from this that $B^{(2)}(u) \underset{B^{(2)}}{\sim} B^{(2)}(w)$ for any u and w such that $B^{(2)}(u) \subseteq B^{(1)}(x)$ and $B^{(2)}(w) \subset B^{(1)}(y)$, that is, in particular, $B^{(2)}(x) \underset{B^{(2)}}{\sim} B^{(2)}(y)$. Hence $x \in B^{(2)}(y)$, that is

$$B^{(1)}*(x) \subseteq B^{(2)}*(x). \tag{2}$$

The juxtaposition of (1) and (2) proves Lemma 3 completely.

Proof of Theorem 4.1 We know that a derivative division is a particular case of a regular extension. Hence it is obvious that $B^{**}(x) = B^{*}(x)$ for any x.

Example of an artificial language in which two elements belong to the same family but to different types.

Suppose we are given a language consisting of the five elements:

$$x, y_1, y_2, z_1, z_2.$$

Suppose we are given the nine registered phrases:

$$\begin{aligned}
A_1 &= y_2 x & A_6 &= z_1 x \\
A_2 &= y_2 y_1 & A_7 &= z_1 z_2 \\
A_3 &= y_1 y_2 & A_8 &= x y_2 \\
A_4 &= x z_1 & A_9 &= z_1 y_1 \\
A_5 &= y_1 z_1 &
\end{aligned}$$

and the following divisions by environments:

$$\begin{aligned}
\Gamma(x) &= \{x\}, \\
\Gamma(y) &= \{y_1, y_2\}, \\
\Gamma(z) &= \{z_1, z_2\}.
\end{aligned}$$

Comparison of A_1 and A_2, A_3 and A_8, A_4 and A_5, A_6 and A_9, leads us to the conclusion that

$$y_1 \sim x \text{ or } x \in S(y_1).$$

Compare their Γ-structures with these phrases. We have the following registered Γ-structures:

$$\Gamma(A_1) = \Gamma(y)\,\Gamma(x) \qquad\qquad \Gamma(A_6) = \Gamma(z)\,\Gamma(x)$$
$$\Gamma(A_3) = \Gamma(A_2) = \Gamma(y)\,\Gamma(y) \qquad \Gamma(A_7) = \Gamma(z)\,\Gamma(z)$$
$$\Gamma(A_4) = \Gamma(x)\,\Gamma(z) \qquad\qquad \Gamma(A_8) = \Gamma(x)\,\Gamma(y)$$
$$\Gamma(A_5) = \Gamma(y)\,\Gamma(z) \qquad\qquad \Gamma(A_9) = \Gamma(z)\,\Gamma(y)$$

Comparing

$$\Gamma(A_1) \text{ and } \Gamma(A_6) \qquad\qquad \Gamma(A_7) \text{ and } \Gamma(A_5)$$
$$\Gamma(A_2) \text{ and } \Gamma(A_5) \qquad\qquad \Gamma(A_8) \text{ and } \Gamma(A_4)$$
$$\Gamma(A_2) \text{ and } \Gamma(A_7) \qquad\qquad \Gamma(A_9) \text{ and } \Gamma(A_2)$$

we come to the conclusion that $\Gamma(z) \underset{\Gamma}{\sim} \Gamma(y)$.

On the other hand, comparing the registered Γ-structure $\Gamma(y)$ $\Gamma(x)$ with the unregistered $\Gamma(x)\,\Gamma(x)$, we come to the conclusion that $\Gamma(y)$ is not Γ-equivalent to $\Gamma(x)$.

Theorem 4.2. In correct languages, for any x,

$$\text{1) } R(x) \subseteq T(x),$$
$$\text{2) } T(x) = R^*(x).$$

Proof. (1) Let x and y belong to one and the same section. This means that, between them, there existed a chain $r_1, r_2, \ldots r_n$, such that, for all i, the elements r_i and r_{i+1} belonged *either* to one and the same environment *or* to one and the same family. If r_i and r_{i+1} belonged to one environment, they must belong to one and the same type, as the division into types is a derivative of the division into environments. If, however, r_i and r_{i+1} belonged to the same family, they belong to the same type, because of correctness. Thus all the elements of the chain remain within the type; the first statement is proved.

(2) Before proving the second part of the Theorem, we prove the following auxiliary statement.

Lemma. In a correct language division into sections coincides with division into environments, or is a regular extension of division into environments.

It is clear that a section can simply coincide with an environment. (This is true of a non-correct language as well.) Suppose there is a section larger than the environment. Then several environments $\Gamma_1, \Gamma_2, \ldots \Gamma_n$ belong to the section. By Theorem 4.2 (Point 1), the whole section is contained in one type, and this means that $\Gamma_i \underset{\Gamma}{\sim} \Gamma_k$.

Hence the division into sections (for the case that the section is larger than the environment) is a regular extension of the division into environments.

Corollary. Applying Lemma 3, p. 175, (for the case that the section does not coincide with the environment) we obtain

$$R^*(x) = \Gamma^*(x) = T(x).$$

But this equation is realized in a trivial manner if the section coincides with the environment. The Theorem is proved.

We now show, by using the example we have analysed, that the requirement of correctness in a language is necessary. It is easy to see that, in the example we have considered, there are these types:

$$T_1 = x$$
$$T_2 = y_1, y_2, z_1, z_2,$$

and the following sections:

$$R_1 = x, y_1, y_2,$$
$$R_2 = z_1, z_2.$$

Compare now each of the phrases A_i, for instance A_1, A_4, A_6, A_7, with the corresponding R-structure. We find that all the possible R-structures from the two elements, for instance,

$$R(A_1) = R_1 R_1,$$
$$R(A_4) = R_1 R_2,$$
$$R(A_6) = R_2 R_1,$$
$$R(A_7) = R_2 R_2,$$

are registered. Hence $R_1 \underset{R}{\sim} R_2$ and all five elements belong to $R^*(x)$, that is $T(x) \subseteq R^*(x)$ and $T(z) \subseteq R^*(z)$. On the other hand, for instance, $x \in T(z)$, that is, here, the derivative for the division into sections does not coincide with the division into types.

Chapter IV §28

Theorem 4.3. (Uspenskii's Theorem). Any formally homogeneous language is a correct language.

Proof. Let $x \in S(y)$, and, for any element $x_1 \in \Gamma(x)$, let it be true that, from the non-emptiness of the intersection $\Gamma(x_1) \cap S(y) = x$, there follows the existence of an element z such that $S(x_1) \cap \Gamma(y) = z$, that is, for any a_i and b_i, from the registration of

$$a_1a_2 \ldots a_k x_1 a_{k+1} \ldots a_n, \tag{1}$$

there follows the registration of

$$a_1a_2 \ldots a_k z a_{k+1} \ldots a_n, \tag{2}$$

and, from the registration of

$$b_1 \ldots b_1 z b_{l+1} \ldots b_m, \tag{3}$$

there follows the registration of

$$b_1 \ldots b_1 x_1 b_{l+1} \ldots b_m. \tag{4}$$

Having considered the corresponding Γ-structures, we at once convince ourselves that, from the registration of $\Gamma(a_1) \ldots \Gamma(a_k)$ $\Gamma(x) \Gamma(a_{k+1}) \ldots \Gamma(a_n)$, there follows the registration of $\Gamma(a_1) \ldots$ $\Gamma(a_k) \Gamma(y) \Gamma(a_{k+1}) \ldots \Gamma(a_n)$, and conversely. Hence $\Gamma(x) \underset{\Gamma}{\sim} \Gamma(y)$, which it was also required to prove.

Note. The condition of homogeneity is by no means essential in order that $\Gamma(x) \underset{\Gamma}{\sim} \Gamma(y)$. It is sufficient that, for any $x_1 \in \Gamma(x)$, there should be an element $z \in \Gamma(y)$ and elements $a_i' \in \Gamma(a_i)$ such that, from the registration of $a_1 \ldots a_k x_1 a_{k+1} \ldots a_n$, there should follow the registration of $a_i' \ldots a_k' z a'_{k+1} \ldots a_n'$, and that the converse should be true for any element $y' \in \Gamma(y)$. For example, it is easy to verify that $\Gamma(okno^{[1]}) \underset{\Gamma}{\sim} \Gamma(metro^{[2]})$, although not one of the words belonging to $\Gamma(okno)$ is equivalent to the word *metro*.

Chapter IV §29

Theorem 4.4. (*a*) the morphological subclasses form a division of the whole set of words; (*b*) the derivative of the division into morphological subclasses coincides with the division into types.

Proof. (*a*) Denote the morphological subclass corresponding to y by M(y). Let $x \in$ M(y); that is, there exists a w such that $w \in \Pi S(x) \cap \Gamma(y)$. By the definition of the subfamily there exists a z such that $z \in S(y) \cap \Gamma(x)$. Let $z \in \overline{\in} \Pi S(y)$; then there will be a word $a \in \Gamma(y)$ for which there exists no d such that $d \in S(a) \cap \Gamma(z)$; but $\Gamma(y) = \Gamma(w)$ and $\Gamma(z) = \Gamma(x)$. So $w \in \Gamma(a) \cap (x)$, but there is no b such that $b \in S(a) \cap \Gamma(x)$. This however contradicts the assumption that $w \in \Pi S(x)$. So $z \in \Pi S(y)$. Hence it follows that, if $x \in$ M(y), then $y \in$ M(x). Now let $x \in$ M(y) and $y \in$ M(z). In other words there exist a and b such that $a \in \Pi S(x) \cap \Gamma(y)$ and $b \in \Pi S(y) \cap \Gamma(z)$.

[1] window   [2] underground railway

Under these conditions $y \in \Gamma(a) \cap \Pi S(b)$. From what has been proved above it follows that there exists a w such that $w \in \Pi S(a) \cap \Gamma(b)$. But $\Pi S(a) = \Pi S(x)$ and $\Gamma(b) = \Gamma(z)$. So $x \in M(z)$. The first part of the statement is proved.

(b) To start with we prove that M-division is a regular extension of Γ-division. Let $\Gamma(x) \subseteq M(y)$. We prove $\Gamma(x) \underset{\Gamma}{\sim} \Gamma(y)$, that is, that, for the arbitrary phrases $A = a_1 \ldots a_k$ and $B = b_1 \ldots b_m$, the structures $\Gamma(A) \, \Gamma(x) \, \Gamma(B)$ and $\Gamma(A) \, \Gamma(y) \, \Gamma(B)$ are at the same time registered or at the same time not registered. Let the first be registered and the second not.

Without restricting generality it may be considered that the phrase $a_1 \ldots a_k x b_1 \ldots b_m$ is registered. In that case, by the condition $x \in M(y)$, it follows that there exists a w such that $w \in \Pi S(x) \cap \Gamma(y)$. If $w \in S(x)$, then the phrase $a_1 \ldots a_k w b_1 \ldots b_m$ is registered. The Γ-structure of this phrase is $\Gamma(A) \, \Gamma(w) \, \Gamma(B)$ and it is registered as the structure of a registered phrase. But, since $\Gamma(w) = \Gamma(y)$, this structure is, by the assumption, not registered. The contradiction that has resulted shows that $\Gamma(x) \underset{\Gamma}{\sim} \Gamma(y)$. Now, applying Lemma 3 (p. 175), we find that $M^*(x) = T(x)$.

Theorem 4.5. If a language is regular, then two words belonging to one morphological subclass belong to the same paradigmatic category.

Proof. Let $x \in M(y)$ and let $K(x)$ be an arbitrary paradigmatic category containing x. By the Condition there exists a word w such that $w \in \Pi S(x) \cap \Gamma(y)$. Because of regularity $w \in K(x)$, and, from $w \in \Gamma(y)$ and the definition of a paradigmatic category, it follows that $y \in K(w)$, where $K(w)$ is an arbitrary paradigmatic category containing w. So $y \in K(x)$. The Theorem is proved.

Theorem 4.6. If a language is formally homogeneous and regular, then the non-paradigmatic categories are uniformly distributed in it.

Proof. Let there be a non-paradigmatic category K such that $x \in N(y)$, $z \in K \cap \Gamma(x)$ and $K \cap \Gamma(y) = 0$. Since $x \in N(y)$ and, by the assumption $\Gamma(x) = \Gamma(z)$, then $\Gamma(z) \cap S(y) \neq 0$. Hence, because of the homogeneity of the language, $S(z) \cap \Gamma(y) \neq 0$ (1). Because of formal homogeneity, the family coincides with the subfamily. Because of regularity $S(z) \subseteq K$. From (1) it follows that there is a w such that $w \in S(z) \cap \Gamma(y)$, and thus $w \in K \cap \Gamma(y)$ and this contradicts our assumption. The Theorem is proved.

Chapter IV §35

Theorem 4.7. In an elementary language, it follows from the condition $S_i \to S_j$ ($S_i \neq S_j$) that at least one S_j-phrase is not an S_i-phrase.

Proof. Assume the opposite. For $S_i \to S_j$, let every S_j-phrase be an S_i-phrase. Let $x \in S_i$ and $y \in S_j$. Since $S(x) \neq S(y)$, there is at least one registered S_j-phrase $A_1 y A_2$ such that the corresponding S_i-phrase $A_1 x A_2$ is not registered.

$S_i \to S_j$ and, by our assumption, the S_j-phrase $A_1 y A_2$ is at the same time an S_i-phrase, that is, the replacement of some element by x must give a registered phrase.

Since $A_1 x A_2$ is not registered, there must be a registered phrase containing both y and x, that is, two words from one elementary category. This is incompatible with the elementariness of the language and proves the statement of the Theorem.

Chapter V §38

Theorem 5.1. A language to which there belongs at least one phrase with frame (i, j) is not a restricted language with a finite mumber of States.

Proof. Let $A = x_1 \ldots x_i x_{i+1} x_{i+2} \ldots x_{j-2} x_{j-1} x_j \ldots x_n$ be a registered phrase with frame (i, j). Then the phrase $A = x_1 \ldots y_i x_{i+1} \ldots x_{j-1} y_j x_{j+1} \ldots x_n$ must also be registered. Between x_i and x_j there are at least two words x_k and x_{k+1} ($i < k < k+1 < j$) standing next to one another at the same distance from the start in both phrases. Consider $k = j - 2$. Owing to the restrictions placed on the language in the production of both phrases, we pass through State $C_{k, k+1}$. But, in the transition to the next State from this, there must be two possibilities of transition into the other State, namely, in the transition to one of them x_j must be produced, and, in the transition to the other, y_j.

But, then, the phrase $A = x_1 \ldots x_i x_{i+1} \ldots x_{j-1} y_j \ldots x_n$ will also be produced by our scheme, that is, it must also be registered, and this contradicts the Condition. The Theorem is proved.

Chapter V §39

Theorem 5.2. (*a*) Every registered S-structure is a complete B-structure; (*b*) If in a stipulated division B every B-structure is *either* not registered *or* complete, then, for any element x, it is true that $B(x) \subseteq S(x)$.

Proof. (*a*) Let a registered S-structure $S(x_1)S(x_2) \ldots S(x_n)$ be given. Without restricting generality it may be taken that it is precisely the phrase $x_1 x_2 \ldots x_n$ that is registered. We prove that the given S-structure is complete, that is, that the arbitrary phrase $y_1 y_2 \ldots y_n$ is registered if only $x_i \in S(y_i)$. Let $y_1 y_2 \ldots y_n$ be not registered. We substitute $x_2 x_3 \ldots x_n$ for $y_2 y_3 \ldots y_n$; then the resulting phrase $y_1 x_2 \ldots x_n$ is not registered, because $x_2 \in S(y_2), \ldots x_n \in S(y_n)$, and is registered because $x_1 \in S(y_1)$. The contradiction that has resulted proved our statement.

(*b*) Let a division B be given in which an arbitrary B-structure is complete *or* not registered, and let $x \in B(y)$. We prove that $x \in S(y)$. Consider the arbitrary phrase

$$CxD. \tag{1}$$

If it is registered then the B-structure

$$B(C)B(x)B(D) \tag{2}$$

is also registered, and this means, by reason of the completeness of (2), that the phrase

$$CyD \tag{3}$$

is also registered.

Similarly, if (1) is not registered, then (2) and (3) are not registered. So (1) and (3) are at the same time registered or not registered, and this means that $x \in S(y)$.

Chapter V §41

Theorem 5.3. For any two constituents of a given sentence in a syntactically correct language R_1 and R_2, one of two things is true: (1) one of them directly subordinates the other; (2) there is a constituent R_3 which subordinates R_2 and directly subordinates R_1.

Proof. Any constituent in a syntactically correct language is either a basic constituent (real or unreal), or an attributive constituent. If both constituents are basic, then, for them, by the definition of the Sentence, the first condition is fulfilled.

Suppose now that one of the constituents, for instance, R_1, is not basic. Then it is an attributive constituent and is directly subordinated to some other one; this latter is, in its turn, attributive or basic; etc. Finally, we come to a basic constituent R_{b_1} such that R_1 is subordinated to R_{b_1}. If $R_2 = R_{b_1}$, then the first condition is fulfilled. Let $R_2 \neq R_{b_1}$. If R_2 is a basic constituent, then R_{b_1} subordinates R_2, and, at the same time, R_{b_1} subordinates R_1, that is, the second condition is fulfilled. Finally, suppose R_2 is not a basic constituent. Repeating the argument constructed at the beginning for R_1, we see that there is a basic constituent R_{b_2} such that R_{b_2} subordinates R_2. R_{b_2} *either* coincides with R_{b_1} *or* subordinates R_{b_1}. In both cases R_{b_2} satisfies the second condition. The Theorem is proved.

Theorem 5.4. In a Sentence there is one and only one predicative pair.

Proof. Consider the process of abbreviating an S-structure which is a sentence. If its basic abbreviation consisted of only one element S_1, then there would correspond to it a constituent R_1 (S_1 itself or a prebasic configuration with resultant S_1) for which there is no other basic constituent, and, consequently, no constituent R_2 such that R_2 subordinated R_1 – and this contradicts the definition of the Sentence. Now suppose that the basic abbreviation consists of n elements, where $n > 2$. Then n basic constituents correspond to them, and each of these will be subordinated to exactly $n-1$ constituents and this contradicts the condition. Only one possibility remains, that is, that the basic constituent consists of exactly two elements and, consequently, there are just two basic constituents. The Theorem is proved.

Theorem 5.5. If a registered S-structure has norm 2, then it is a a sentence.

Proof. (From the Opposite.) Suppose that the S-structure has the norm 2 and that, for some constituent R_1, there is no constituent R_2 such that $R_2 \rightarrow R_1$. Then R_1 cannot be an attributive constituent. Now let R_1 be a basic constituent. But then, by our assumption, it is the only basic constituent, and the S-structure has the norm 1.

Chapter V §43

Theorem 5.6. If a language is given as a finite set of registered phrases, then not a single regular configuration of the first rank can be determined in it.

Proof. (From the Opposite.) Let there be at least one regular configuration of the first rank in our language; for simplicity, we consider a configuration of two elements B_1B_2, with the Resultant B_2. This means that, for any structures of the phrases A_1 and A_2, the B-structures

$$B(A_1)B_1B_2B(A_2) \tag{1}$$

and

$$B(A_1)B_2B(A_2), \tag{2}$$

are simultaneously registered; that is, in other words, wherever the element B_2 occurs, it is always possible to place an element B_1 in front of it such that the resulting structure will be registered. Consider Structure (1) and, in it, replace the element B_2 by B_1B_2; the resulting structure

$$B(A_1)B_1B_1B_2B(A_2) \tag{3}$$

must also be registered. Instead of the one element B_1 we have B_1B_1. Repeat the same operation with Structure (3). As the Set of phrases is finite we finally come to a B-structure such as

$$B(A_1)\underbrace{B_1 \ldots B_1}_{k \text{ times}}B_2B(A_2), \tag{4}$$

which is registered, whereas the B-structure

$$B(A_1)\underbrace{B_1 \ldots B_1}_{k+1 \text{ times}}B_2B(A_2) \tag{5}$$

cannot any longer be registered.

Denote $B(A_1)\underbrace{B_1 \ldots B_1}_{k+\text{times}}$ by $B(C_1)$. Then (4) and (5) take the form

$$B(C_1)B_2B(A_2), \tag{4a}$$

$$B(C_1)B_1B_2B(A_2). \tag{5a}$$

Here (4*a*) is a registered structure, whereas (5*a*) is not registered. This contradicts the assumption that B_1B_2 is a configuration with the Resultant B_2. The Theorem is proved.

Chapter V §46

Theorem 5.7. If a rearrangement in a simple and formally homogeneous language satisfies the requirement of semantic connection, then it is a transformation.

First of all we prove the following auxiliary statement:

Lemma. If a word x in a simple formally homogeneous language belongs to a unitary environment, then any word y such that $y \in S(x)$ also belongs to the unitary environment.

Proof. Let $\Gamma(x) = \{x\}$ and $y \in S(x)$. Let $y' \neq y$ and $y' \in \Gamma(y)$. Hence it follows that $y \in \Gamma(y') \cap S(x)$. Because of homogeneity, there is a word x' such that $x' \in S(y') \cap \Gamma(x)$. This means that $x' = x$. So $S(x) = S(y_1)$, and two different words y and y' belong to $\Gamma(y) \cap S(y)$. This however contradicts the condition of simplicity. The Lemma is proved.

Note. The Lemma is also interesting from the point of view of the linguistic interpretation. Since a word that belongs to a unitary environment is, according to our interpretation, a subsidiary word, we have proved that a word which is equivalent to a subsidiary word is itself a subsidiary word.

We pass on to the proof of the Theorem. Suppose that two phrases A and B are linked by the conditions of semantic linking. We want to show that any phrase A′ which has the same structure as A is semantically linked with a phrase B′ which has the same structure as B. It is clearly sufficient for us to prove that, on the replacement of one word belonging to a non-unitary environment by an arbitrary word from the same family, a corresponding phrase B′ will arise; for the proof will automatically be extended to the general case with the help of the method of complete induction.

So we replace the first word from A by an arbitrary word from the same family, and in this way obtain the phrase A′. If this word belonged to a unitary environment, then, in accordance with the Lemma, the word which has replaced it belongs to the unitary environment, and we can simply take phrase B as phrase B′, which last satisfies the condition of semantic linking. If however the word that is being replaced (denote it by x_1 and the word that replaces it by v_1) belonged to a non-unitary environment, then we know, first, that there was a y_1 in phrase B such that $x_1 \in \Gamma(y_1)$ and, secondly, that $x_1 \in S(v_1)$. So $x_1 \in \Gamma(y_1) \cap S(v_1)$, and this means that, because of homogeneity, there exists a word z_1 such that $z_1 \in \Gamma(v_1) \cap S(y_1)$. Since $z_1 \in S(y_1)$, if we replace y_1 by z_1 in B, we obtain the registered phrase B'. This phrase is semantically linked with A' since $z_1 \in \Gamma(v_1)$. On the basis of the above remarks we consider that the Theorem is proved.

INDEXES

Index of Terms: references are to paragraph numbers

Index of Names: references are to paragraph numbers

Index of Languages: references are to paragraph numbers